200
PERPLEXING
CHESS
PUZZLES

200
PERPLEXING
CHESS
PUZZLES

Edited
by
Martin Greif

Sterling Publishing Co., Inc. New York

Library of Congress Cataloging-in-Publication Data Available

10 9 8 7 6 5 4 3 2 1

Published by Sterling Publishing Company, Inc.
387 Park Avenue South, New York, N.Y. 10016
© 1997 by Sterling Publishing Company, Inc.
Distributed in Canada by Sterling Publishing
% Canadian Manda Group, One Atlantic Avenue, Suite 105
Toronto, Ontario, Canada M6K 3E7
Distributed in Great Britain and Europe by Cassell PLC
Wellington House, 125 Strand, London WC2R 0BB, England
Distributed in Australia by Capricorn Link (Australia) Pty Ltd.
P.O. Box 6651, Baulkham Hills, Business Centre, NSW 2153, Australia
Manufactured in the United States of America

Sterling ISBN 0-8069-9727-3

CONTENTS

INTRODUCTION

It is unlikely that whoever first formulated the rules of chess on the banks of the Ganges long ago foresaw the emergence of chess problems as an absorbing pastime in their own right. However, in some ways chess problems have exercised an even wider fascination than the game itself, appealing as they do not only to chess players but also to millions for whom the competitive game holds less attraction. Following hard on the heels of the previous four books in this popular series from Sterling Publishing - *200 Classic Chess Puzzles* (1993), *200 Challenging Chess Puzzles* (1995), *200 Demanding Chess Puzzles* (1996), *200 Intriguing Chess Puzzles* (1996) *and* - the present volume, *200 Perplexing Chess Puzzles* (1997), is a collection of some more of the most absorbing chess problems ever devised.

The object in chess, of course, is to trap, or checkmate, the opponent's King into a check from which it cannot escape, thus bringing the game to a victorious conclusion. *200 Perplexing Chess Puzzles* is a collection of gripping, grueling, and teeth-grating end games in which a checkmate, or mate, is required in two, three, four, or more moves. Shown the illustration of a board with chess pieces in fixed positions, it's up to you to determine how to take the King in a given number of moves. What's more, if you're to solve the puzzle successfully, you have to take the part of both players, seeing the game from the point of view of both Black and White. In these riveting chess puzzles, you'll be forced to play the end game both aggressively and defensively, keeping the pieces of both opponents concentrated in logical cooperation until you can say with certainty, "the King is dead," the literal meaning of the Persian *shah mat*, from which the term "checkmate" derives.

200 Perplexing Chess Puzzles is intended for both the player with only an elementary understanding of the game and for the more advanced player who wishes to test his skill. Since the end game is the most important phase of chess, and a good end-game player can vanquish the opening or middle-game specialist, concentrating on these brilliant puzzles will not only provide hours of brain-teasing fun, but may help you to be a better end-game player and enable you to enjoy the challenging endings and therefore chess to the full. Included in the puzzles are Pawn endings, Queen endings, Queen and Pawn endings, Rook and Pawn endings, and minor piece endings. *200 Perplexing Chess Puzzles*, all culled from award-winning chess problems from the past, forces you to play end games that are full of excitement, color, brilliance, and subtlety. And, if you're stumped, or even if you're not, the solutions appear in the back of the book.

A word or two about these solutions is in order. First, the shorthand used to describe chess play in these pages is a modified form of standard Descriptive (or English) Notation, with a dash (—) indicating moves (e.g. P—K4) and an *x* indicating captures (e.g. Q x B). Such abbreviations as *ch*, *db ch*, and *dis ch* (check, double check, and discovers [reveals] check) are obvious, while the beginner may, perhaps, need to be reminded that *e.p.* stands for a capture *en passant*.

Second, since many of the puzzles allow for *more* than one solution, alternative solutions — frequently more than one — are offered. These alternative solutions and moves are indicated by asterisks (*, **, or ***).

Finally, several of the puzzles are not only tricky in their own right, but tricky by design — that is, while the correct solution might call for, say, four moves, you might in fact give mate in only three. The challenge lies in finding the *stipulated* number of moves, even if there is an easier way! With this caveat in mind, enjoy these 200 classic chess challenges to the full.

PUZZLES

PUZZLE No. 1
Black

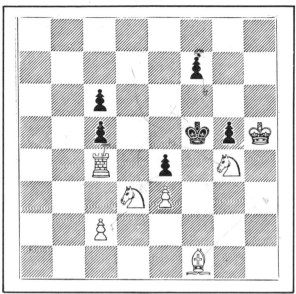

White
White to play and mate in four moves.

PUZZLE No. 2
Black

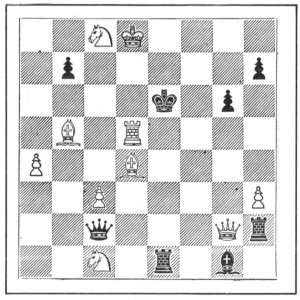

White
White to play and mate in four moves.

11

PUZZLE No. 3
Black

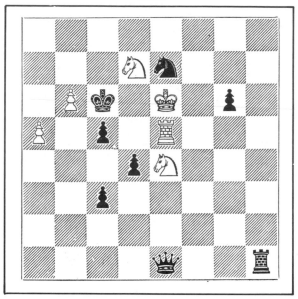

White
White to play and mate in five moves.

PUZZLE No. 4
Black

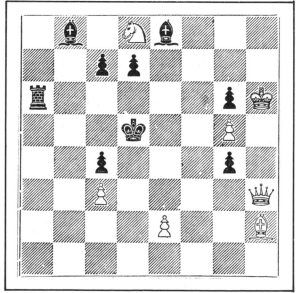

White
White to play and mate in six moves.

PUZZLE No. 5
Black

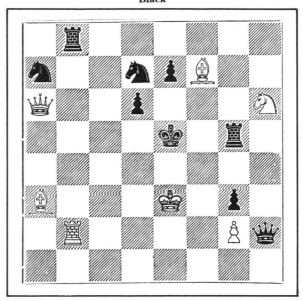

White
White to play and mate in five moves.

PUZZLE No. 6
Black

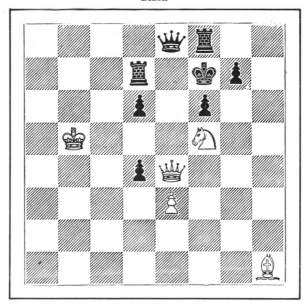

White
White to play and mate in five moves.

White
White to play and mate in four moves.

PUZZLE No. 8
Black

White
White to play and mate in six moves.

PUZZLE No. 9
Black

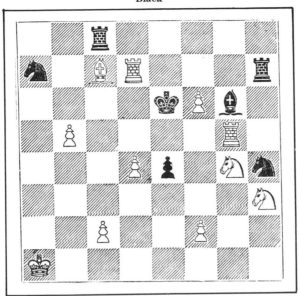

White
White to play and mate in five moves.

PUZZLE No. 10
Black

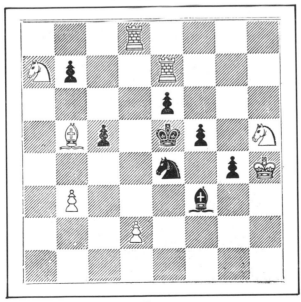

White
White to play and mate in four moves.

15

PUZZLE No. 11
Black

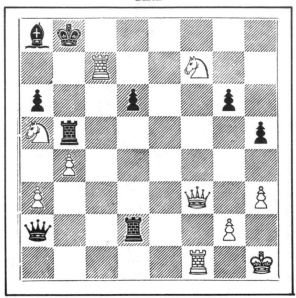

White
White to play and mate in five moves.

PUZZLE No. 12
Black

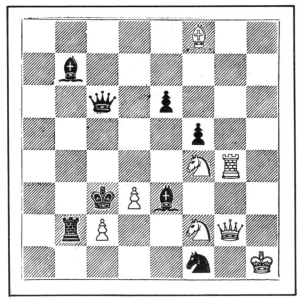

White
White to play and mate in five moves.

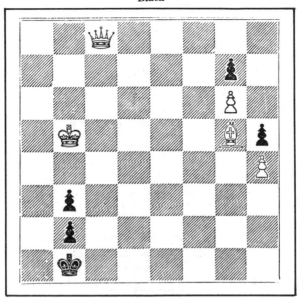

White
White to play and mate in four moves.

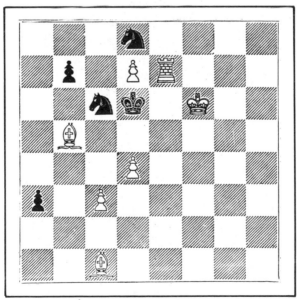

White
White to play and mate in seven moves.

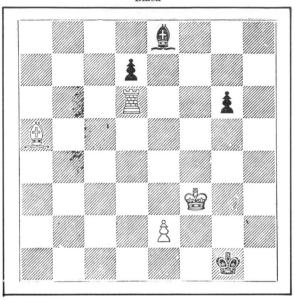

White
White to play and mate in three moves.

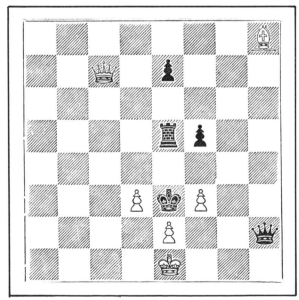

White
White to play and mate in six moves.

PUZZLE No. 17
Black

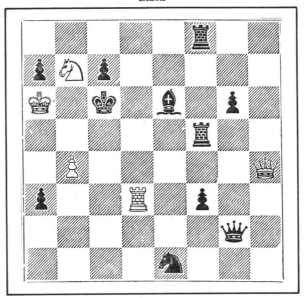

White
White to play and mate in four moves.

PUZZLE No. 18
Black

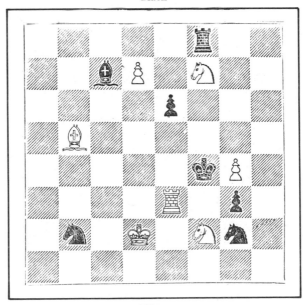

White
White to play and mate in five moves.

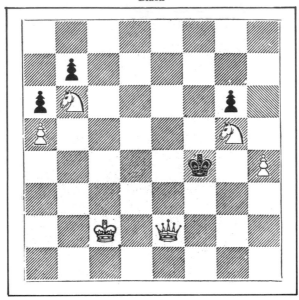

White
White to play and mate in four moves.

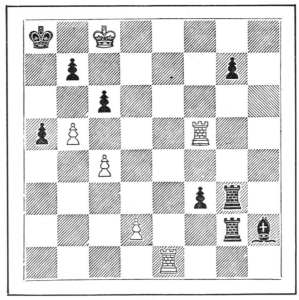

White
White to play and mate in six moves.

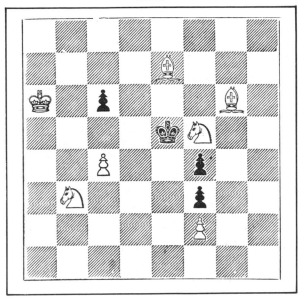

White
White to play and mate in four moves.

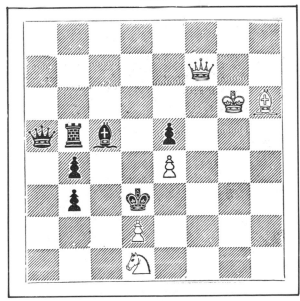

White
White to play and mate in four moves.

White
White to play and mate in three moves.

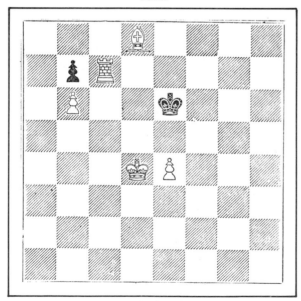

White
White to play and mate in four moves.

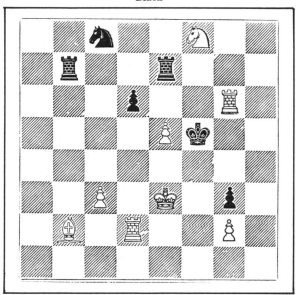

White
White to play and mate in five moves.

PUZZLE No. 26
Black

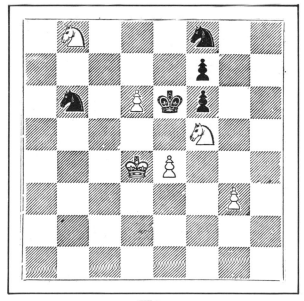

White
White to play and mate in four moves.

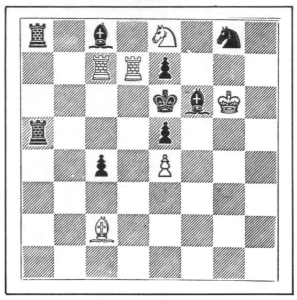

White
White or Black to play and mate in four moves.

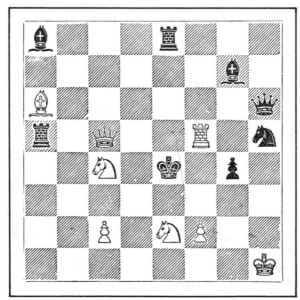

White
White to play and mate in four moves.

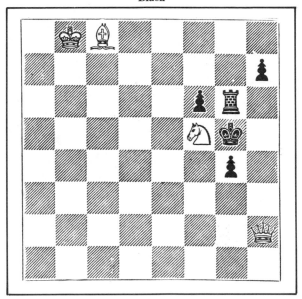

White
White to play and mate in three moves.

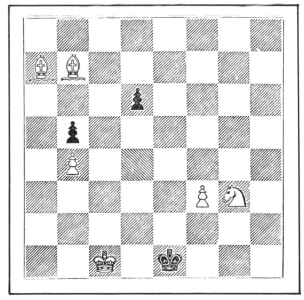

White
White to play and mate in five moves.

PUZZLE No. 31
Black

White
White to play and mate in four moves.

PUZZLE No. 32
Black

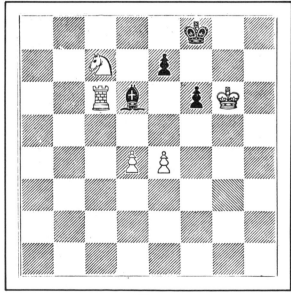

White
White to play and mate in five moves.

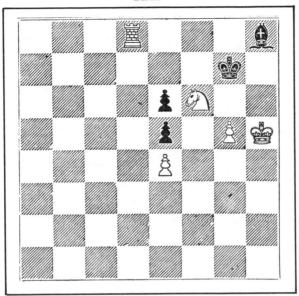

White
White to play and mate in three moves.

PUZZLE No. 34
Black

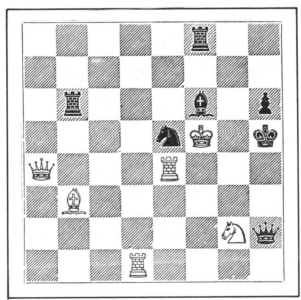

White
White to play and mate in five moves.

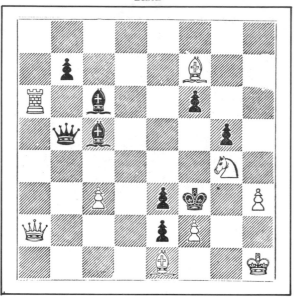

White
White to play and mate in five moves.

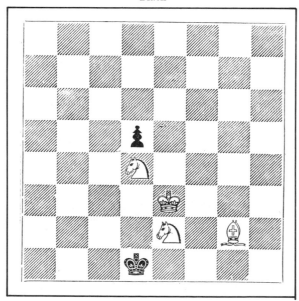

White
White to play and mate in five moves.

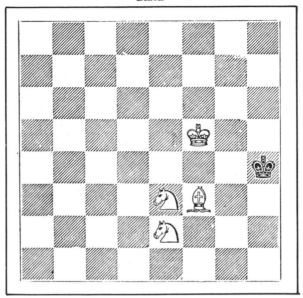

White
White to play and mate in four moves.

PUZZLE No. 38
Black

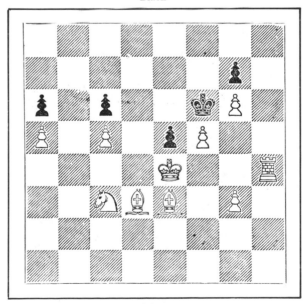

White
White to play and mate in four moves.

PUZZLE No. 39
Black

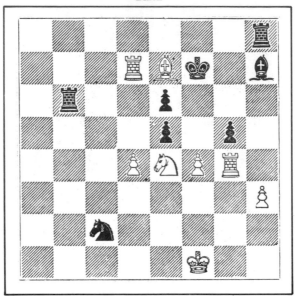

White
White to play and mate in four moves.

PUZZLE No. 40
Black

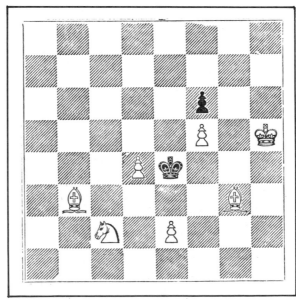

White
White to play and mate in four moves.

PUZZLE No. 41
Black

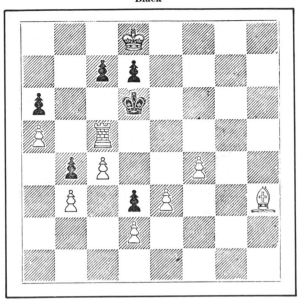

White
White to play and mate in four moves.

PUZZLE No. 42
Black

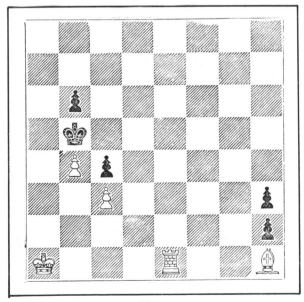

White
White to play and mate in six moves.

PUZZLE No. 43
Black

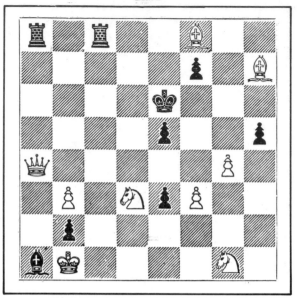

White
White to play and mate in seven moves.

PUZZLE No. 44
Black

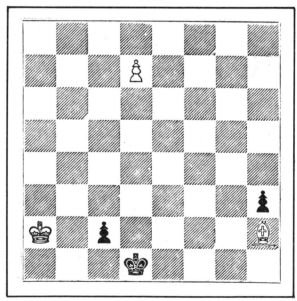

White
White to play and win.

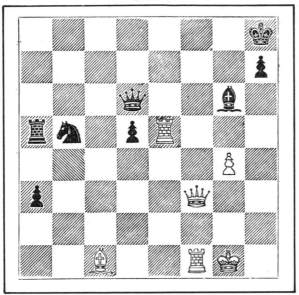

White
White to play and mate in six moves.

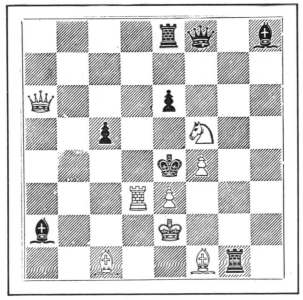

White
White to play and mate in five moves.

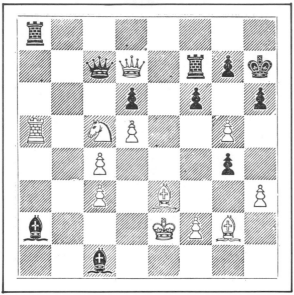

White
White to play and mate in six moves.

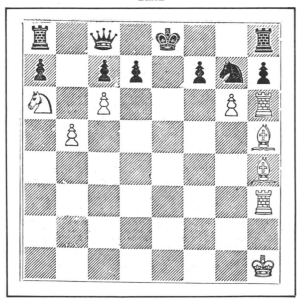

White
White to play and mate in five moves.

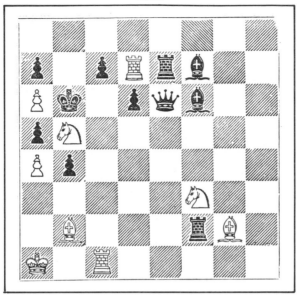

White
White to play and mate in five moves.

PUZZLE No. 50
Black

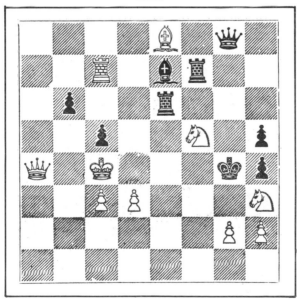

White
White to play and mate in six moves.

PUZZLE No. 51
Black

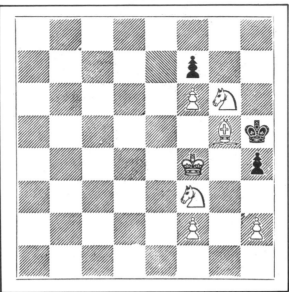

White
White to play and mate in five moves.

PUZZLE No. 52
Black

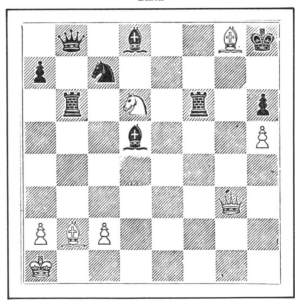

White
White to play and mate in seven moves.

36

PUZZLE No. 53
Black

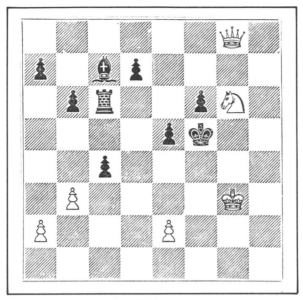

White
White to play and mate in five moves.

PUZZLE No. 54
Black

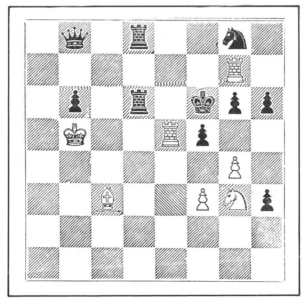

White
White to play and mate in five moves.

PUZZLE No. 55
Black

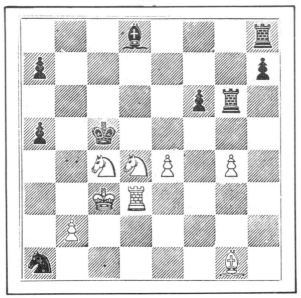

White
White to play and mate in six moves.

PUZZLE No. 56
Black

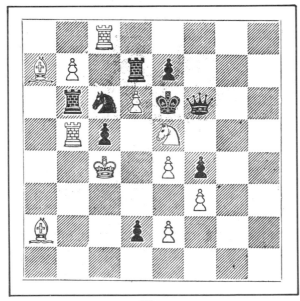

White
White to play and mate in four moves.

PUZZLE No. 57
Black

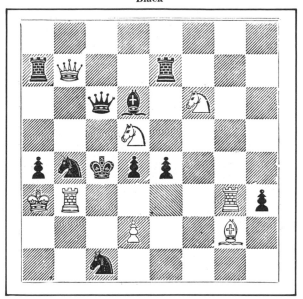

White
White to play and mate in six moves.

PUZZLE No. 58
Black

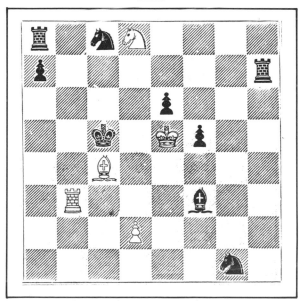

White
White to play and mate in five moves.

PUZZLE No. 59
Black

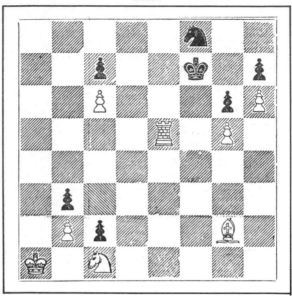

White
White to play and mate in seven moves.

PUZZLE No. 60
Black

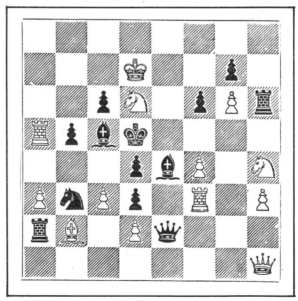

White
White to play and mate in six moves.

PUZZLE No. 61
Black

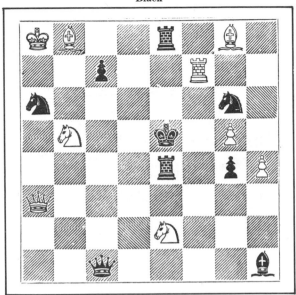

White
White to play and mate in five moves.

PUZZLE No. 62
Black

White
White to play and mate in four moves.

PUZZLE No. 63
Black

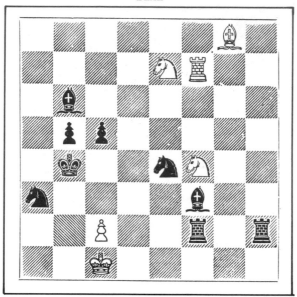

White
White to play and mate in five moves.

PUZZLE No. 64
Black

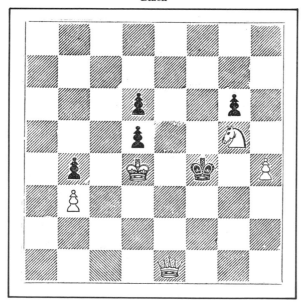

White
White to play and mate in four moves.

PUZZLE No. 65
Black

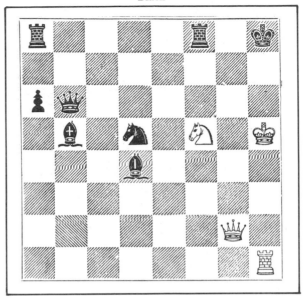

White
White to play and mate in six moves.

PUZZLE No. 66
Black

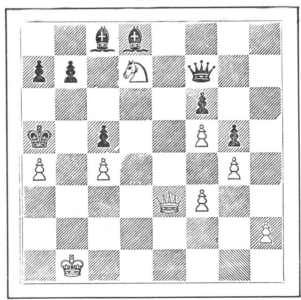

White
White to play and mate in four moves.

43

PUZZLE No. 67
Black

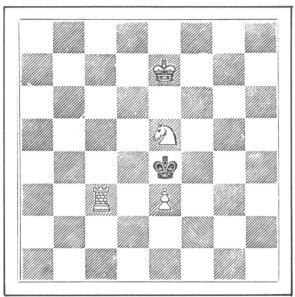

White
White to play and mate in five moves.

PUZZLE No. 68
Black

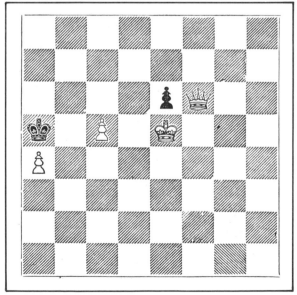

White
White to play and mate in four moves.

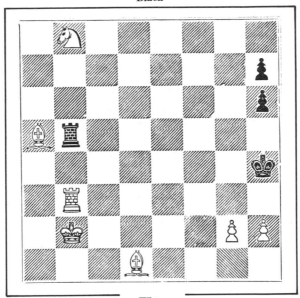

White
White to play and mate with KKtP in six
moves.

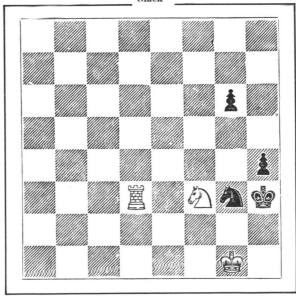

White
White to play and mate in four moves.

PUZZLE No. 71
Black

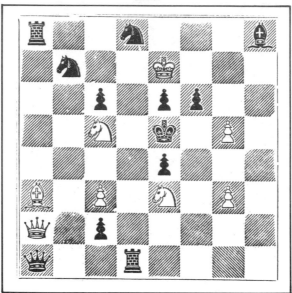

White
White to play and mate in five moves.

PUZZLE No. 72
Black

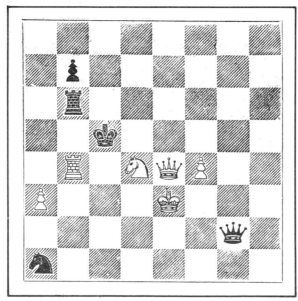

White
White to play and mate in four moves.

46

PUZZLE No. 73
Black

White
White to play and mate in five moves.

PUZZLE No. 74
Black

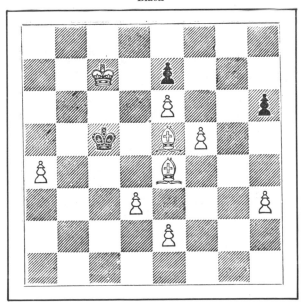

White
White to play and mate in five moves.

PUZZLE No. 75
Black

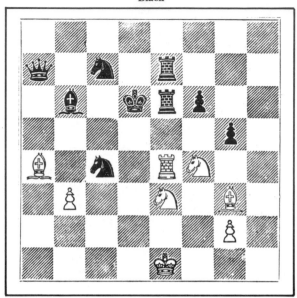

White
White to play and mate in five moves.

PUZZLE No. 76
Black

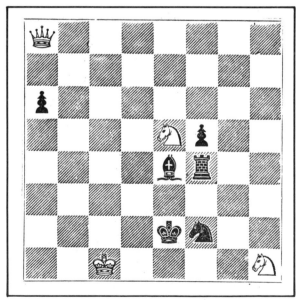

White
White to play and mate in four moves.

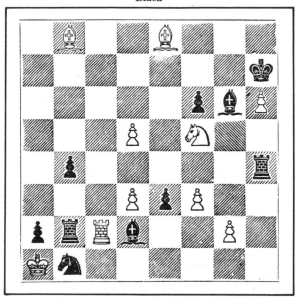

White
White to play and mate in five moves.

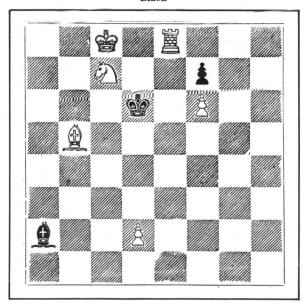

White
White to play and mate in five moves.

PUZZLE No. 79
Black

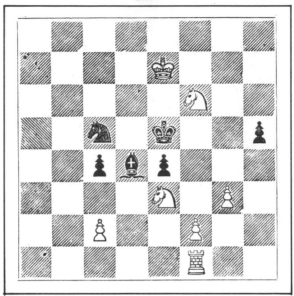

White
White to play and mate in three moves.

PUZZLE No. 80
Black

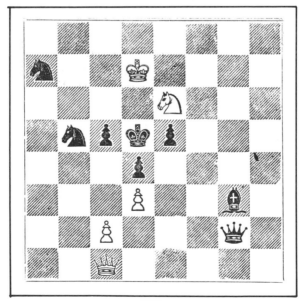

White
White to play and mate in three moves.

PUZZLE No. 81
Black

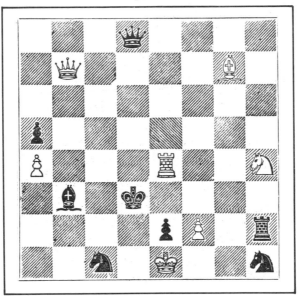

White
White to play and mate in three moves.

PUZZLE No. 82
Black

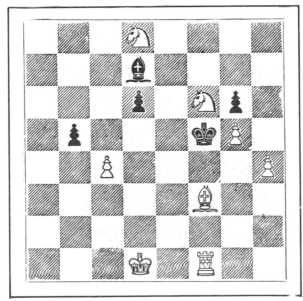

White
White to play and mate in five moves.

51

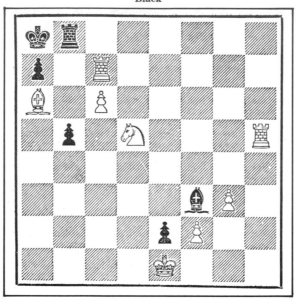

White
White to play and mate in three moves.

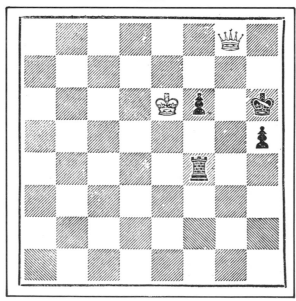

White
White to play and mate in three moves.

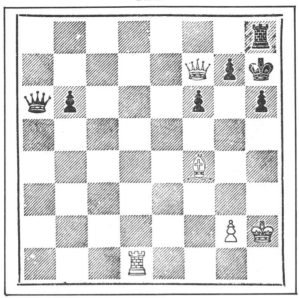

White
White to play and mate in five moves.

White
White to play and mate in four moves.

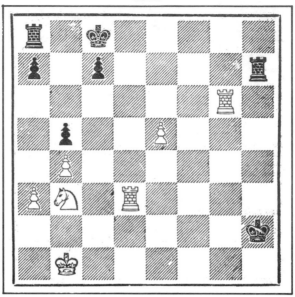

White
White to play and mate in four moves.

PUZZLE No. 88
Black

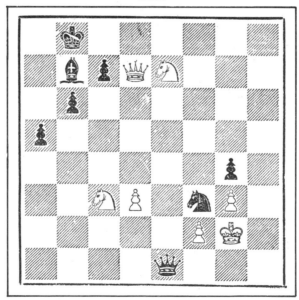

White
White to play and mate in eight moves.

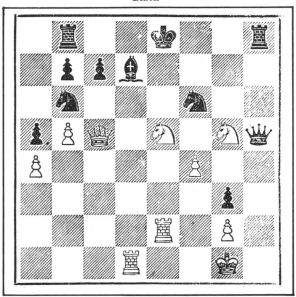

White
White to play and mate in four moves.

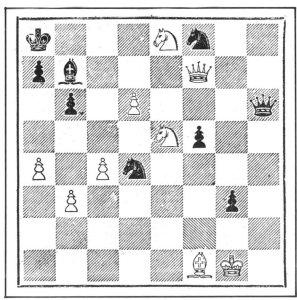

White
White to play and mate in seven moves.

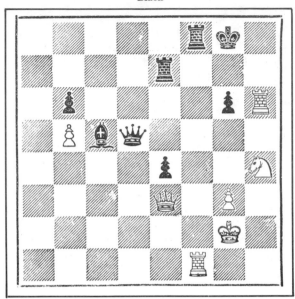

White
White to play and mate in five moves.

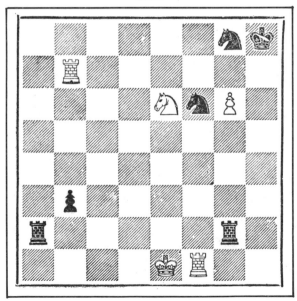

White .
White to play and mate in three moves.

PUZZLE No. 93
Black

White
White to play and mate with P in four moves.

PUZZLE No. 94
Black

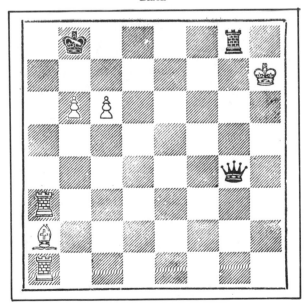

White
White to play and mate with P in four moves.

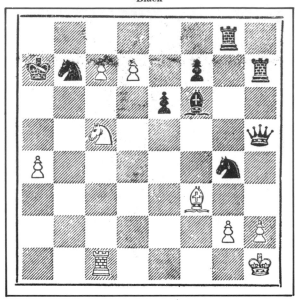

White
White to play and mate in six moves.

White
White to play and mate with P in six moves.

PUZZLE No. 97
Black

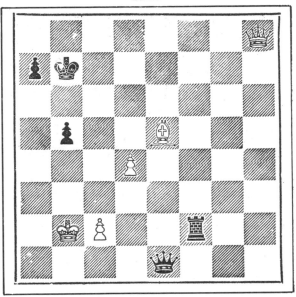

White
White to play and mate in ten moves.

PUZZLE No. 98
Black

White
White to play and mate in five moves.

59

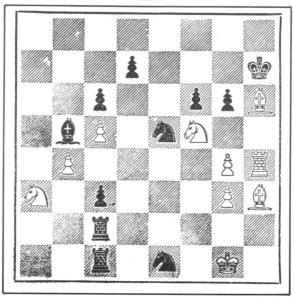

White
White to play and mate in fifteen moves.

White
White to play and mate with KtP in five
moves.

PUZZLE No. 101
Black

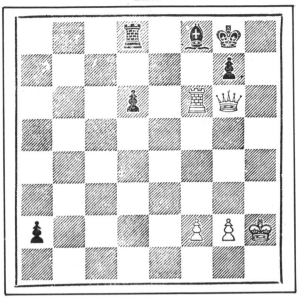

White
White to play and mate in four moves.

PUZZLE No. 102
Black

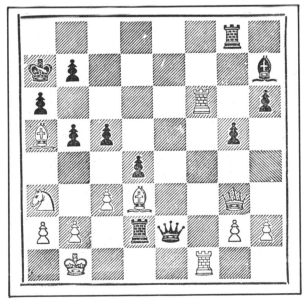

White
White to play and mate in eight moves.

PUZZLE No. 103
Black

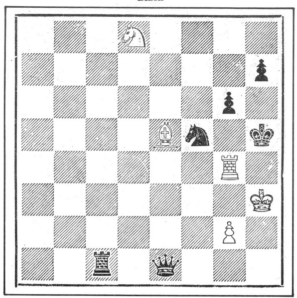

White
White to play and mate in three moves.

PUZZLE No. 104
Black

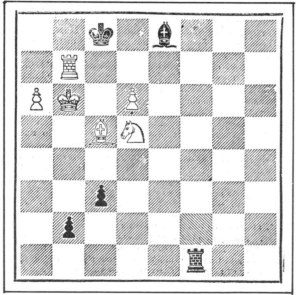

White
White to take all Black's P's with KKtP and
mate with same P in thirteen moves

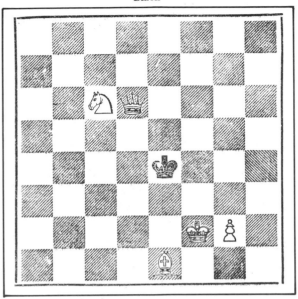

White
White to play and mate with P in four moves.

PUZZLE No. 106
Black

White
White to play and mate in five moves.

White
White forces Black to mate in five moves.

PUZZLE No. 108
Black

White
White to play and mate with P in eight moves.

PUZZLE No. 109
Black

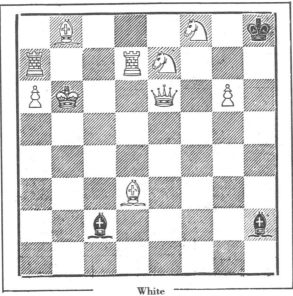

White

White to play and mate with P in thirteen
moves, losing all his men in play except K and
that P.

PUZZLE No. 110
Black

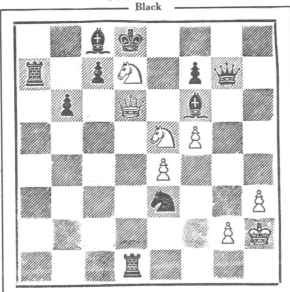

White

White to play and mate with RP in nine
moves.

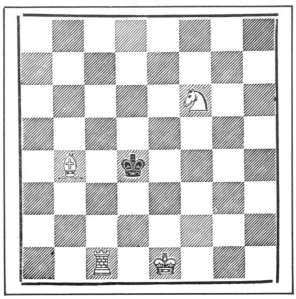

White
White to play and mate in four moves.

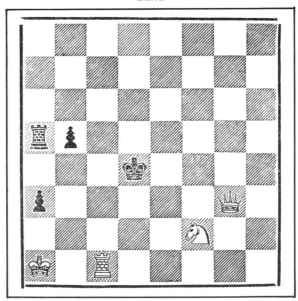

White
White to play and compel Black to mate in six
moves.

PUZZLE No. 113
Black

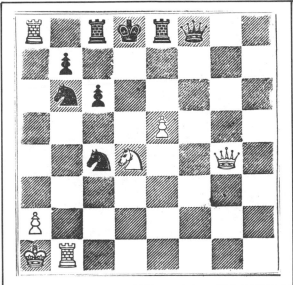

White
White to play and mate in four moves,
checking every move and forcing Black to do
the same.

PUZZLE No. 114
Black

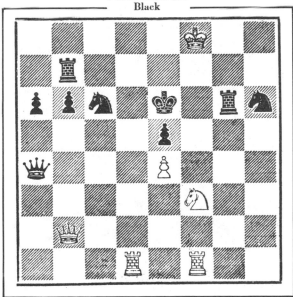

White
White to play and mate in three moves.

PUZZLE No. 115
Black

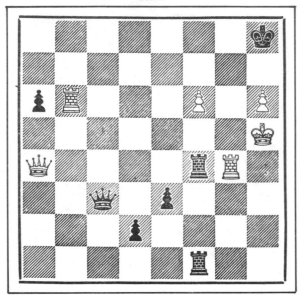

White
White to play and mate with P in six moves.

PUZZLE No. 116
Black

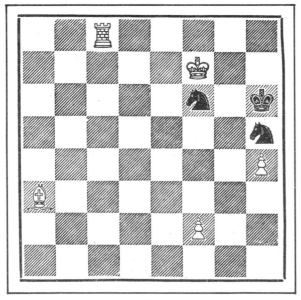

White
White to play and mate in four moves.

PUZZLE No. 117
Black

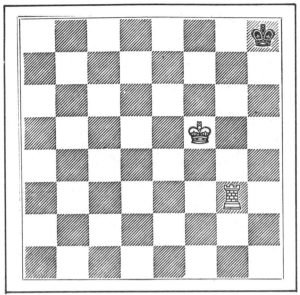

White
White to play and mate in five moves.

PUZZLE No. 118
Black

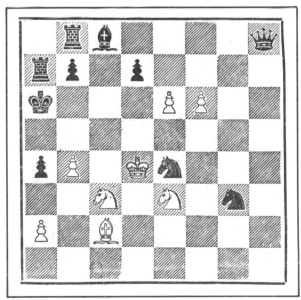

White
White to play and mate in seven moves.

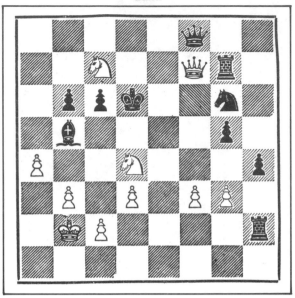

White
White to play and mate in three moves.

PUZZLE No. 120
Black

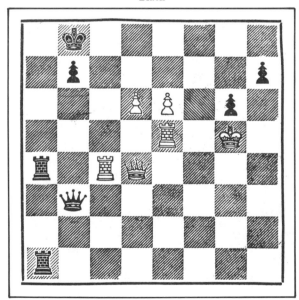

White
White to play and mate in four moves.

PUZZLE No. 121
Black

White
White to play and mate in five moves.

PUZZLE No. 122
Black

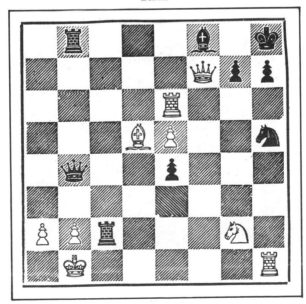

White
White to play and mate in five moves.

PUZZLE No. 123
Black

White
White to play and mate in five moves.

PUZZLE No. 124
Black

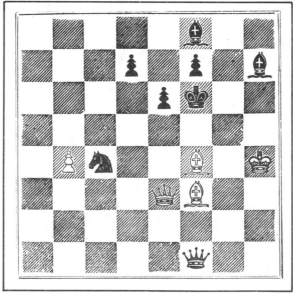

White
White to play and mate in five moves.

72

PUZZLE No. 125
Black

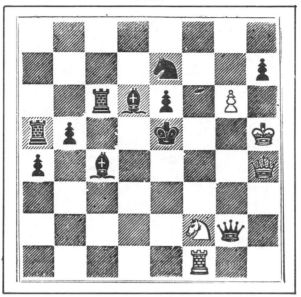

White
White to play and mate in five moves.

PUZZLE No. 126
Black

White
White to play and mate in four moves.

PUZZLE No. 127
Black

White
White to play and mate in four moves.

PUZZLE No. 128
Black

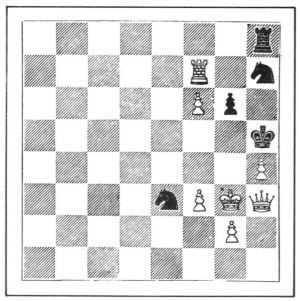

White
White to play and mate in six moves.

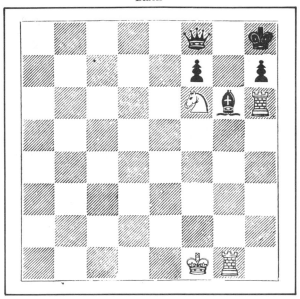

White
White to play and mate in four moves.

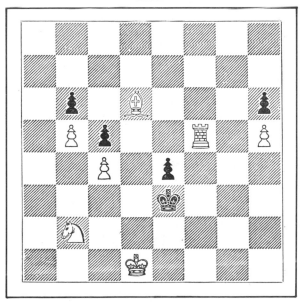

White
White to play and mate in four moves.

White
White to play and mate in seven moves.

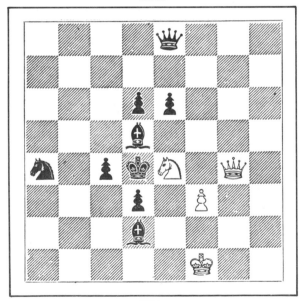

White
White to play and mate in five moves.

PUZZLE No. 133
Black

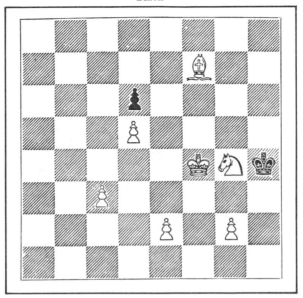

White
White to play and mate in six moves.

PUZZLE No. 134
Black

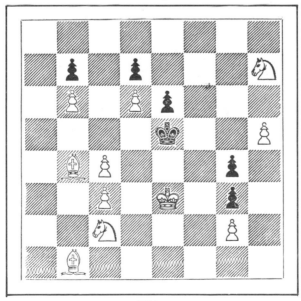

White
White to play and mate in four moves.

PUZZLE No. 135
Black

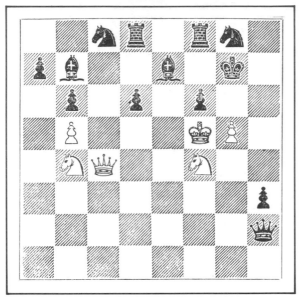

White
White to play and mate in eight moves.

PUZZLE No. 136
Black

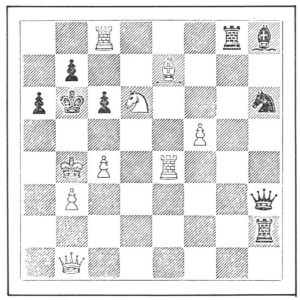

White
White to play and mate in nine moves.

PUZZLE No. 137
Black

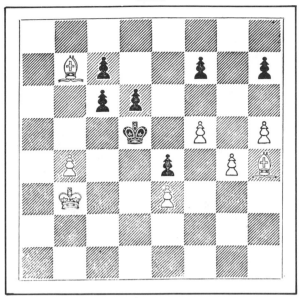

White
White to play and mate in four moves.

PUZZLE No. 138
Black

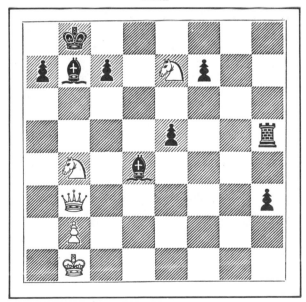

White
White to play and mate in four moves.

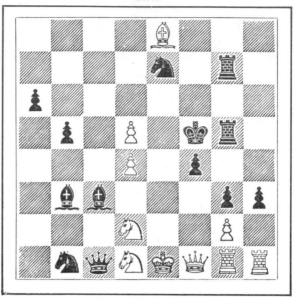

White
White to play and mate in six moves.

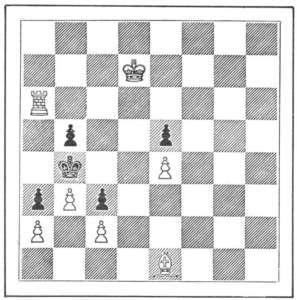

White
White to play and mate in four moves.

PUZZLE No. 141
Black

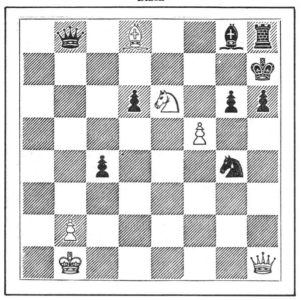

White
White to play and mate in three moves.

PUZZLE No. 142
Black

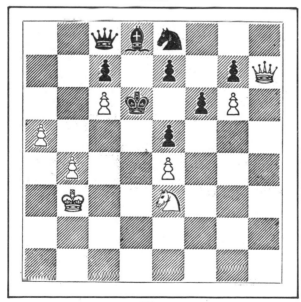

White
White to play and mate in four moves.

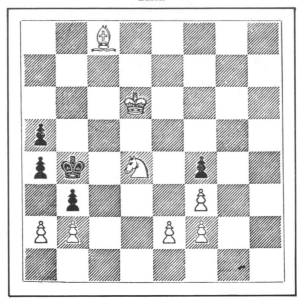

White
White to play and mate in four moves.

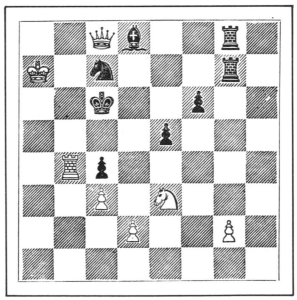

White
White to play and mate in five moves.

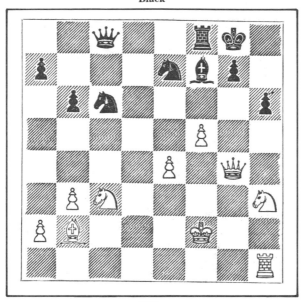

White
White to play and mate in seven moves.

PUZZLE No. 146
Black

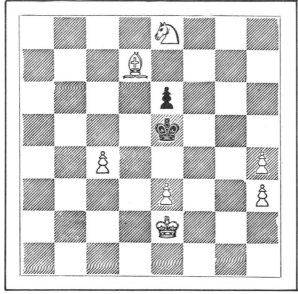

White
White to play and mate in four moves.

PUZZLE No. 147
Black

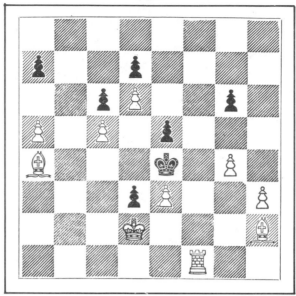

White
White to play and mate in four moves.

PUZZLE No. 148
Black

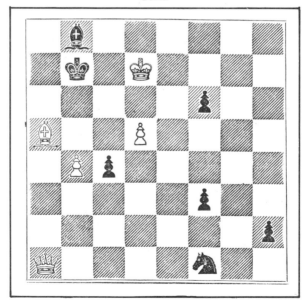

White
White to play and mate in four moves.

84

PUZZLE No. 149
Black

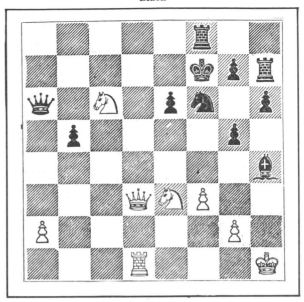

White
White to play and mate in six moves.

PUZZLE No. 150
Black

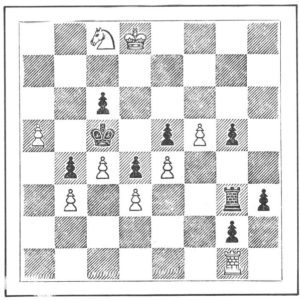

White
White to play and mate in three moves.

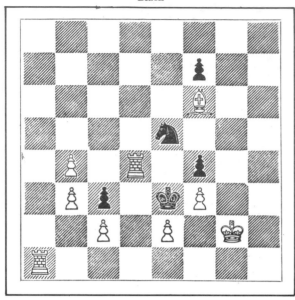

White
White to play and mate in three moves.

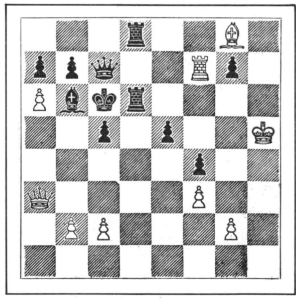

White
White to play and mate in six moves.

PUZZLE No. 153
Black

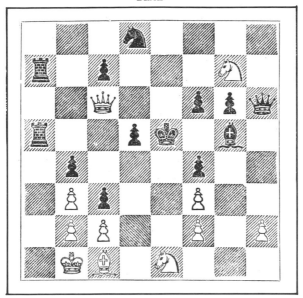

White
White to play and mate in five moves.

PUZZLE No. 154
Black

White
White to play and mate in four moves.

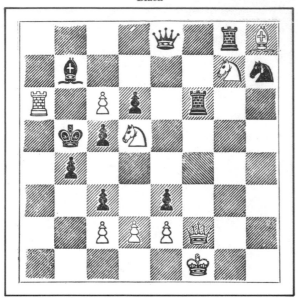

White
White to play and mate in five moves.

White
White to play and mate in three moves.

White
White to play and mate in three moves.

White
White to play and mate in eight moves.

PUZZLE No. 159
Black

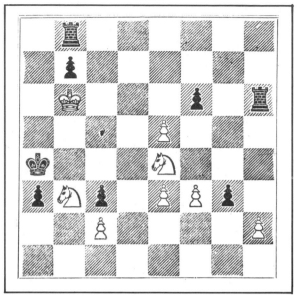

White
White to play and mate in seven moves.

PUZZLE No. 160
Black

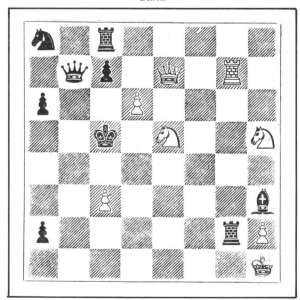

White
White to play and mate in five moves.

White
White to play and mate in five moves.

PUZZLE No. 162
Black

White
White to play and mate in five moves.

PUZZLE No. 163
Black

White
White to play and mate in five moves.

PUZZLE No. 164
Black

White
White to play and mate in two moves.

PUZZLE No. 165
Black

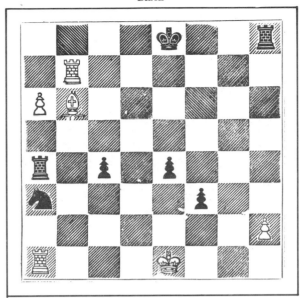

White
White to play and mate in five moves.

PUZZLE No. 166
Black

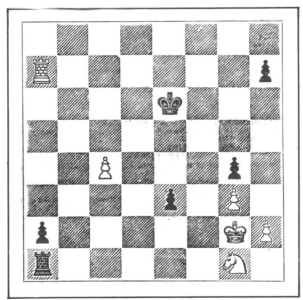

White
Black to play and win.

PUZZLE No. 167
Black

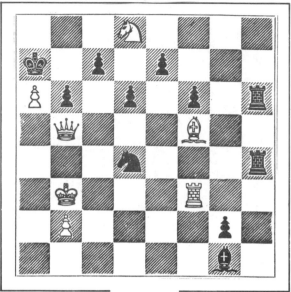

White

Black to ch both K and Q whereupon White
to play and mates in eight moves.

PUZZLE No. 168
Black

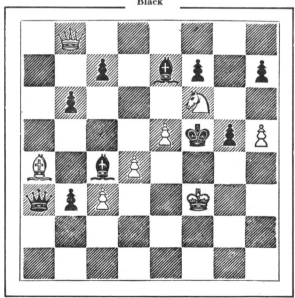

White

White to play and mate in four moves.

PUZZLE No. 169
Black

White
White to play and mate in three moves.

PUZZLE No. 170
Black

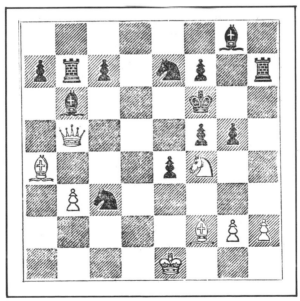

White
White to play and mate in five moves.

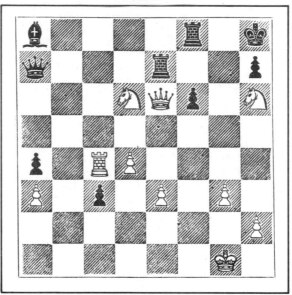

White
White to play and mate in five moves.

PUZZLE No. 172
Black

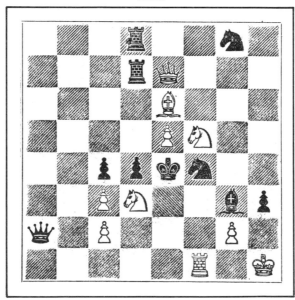

White
White to play and mate in five moves.

White
White to play and mate in six moves.

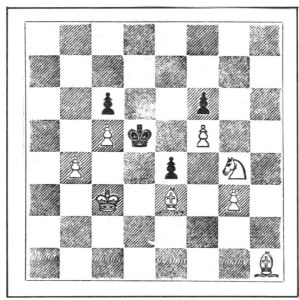

White
White to play and mate in four moves.

PUZZLE No. 175
Black

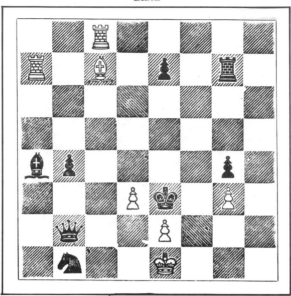

White
White to play and mate in four moves.

PUZZLE No. 176
Black

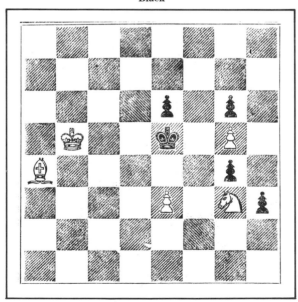

White
White to play and mate in six moves.

98

PUZZLE No. 177
Black

White
White to compel Black to stalepmate him in
eight moves.

PUZZLE No. 178
Black

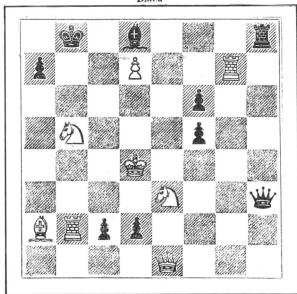

White
White to play and mate in seven moves.

99

White
White to play and mate in five moves.

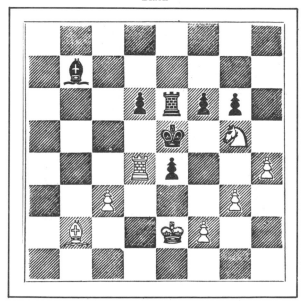

White
White to play and mate in five moves.

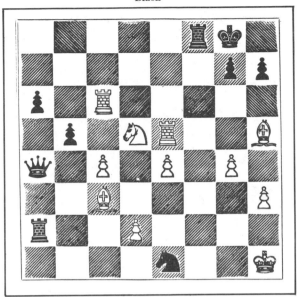

White
White to play and mate in five moves.

White
White to play and mate in seven moves.

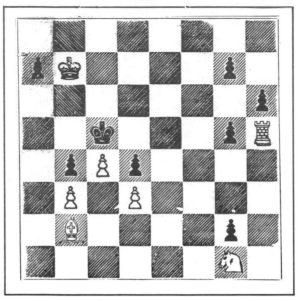

White
White to play and mate in four moves.

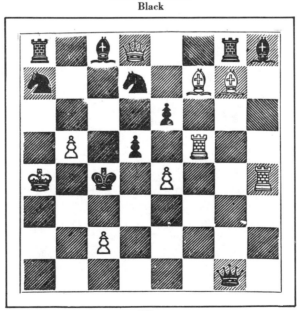

White
White to play and mate in six moves.

PUZZLE No. 185
Black

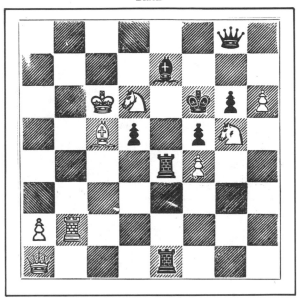

White
White to play and mate in four moves.

PUZZLE No. 186
Black

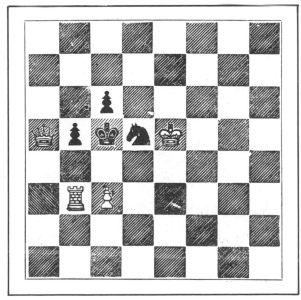

White
White to play and mate in six moves.

PUZZLE No. 187
Black

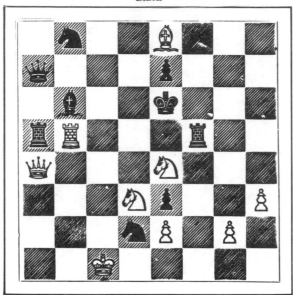

White
White to play and mate in five moves.

PUZZLE No. 188
Black

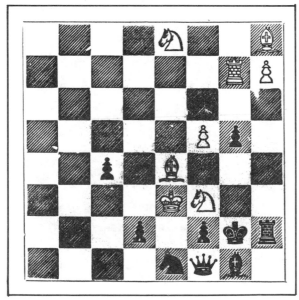

White
White to play and mate in seven moves.

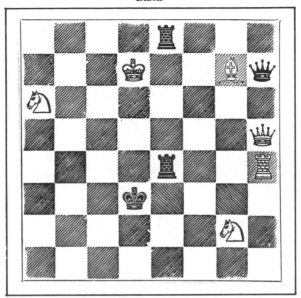

White
White to play and mate in four moves.

White
White to play and mate in six moves.

White
White to play and mate in four moves.

White
White to play and mate in four moves.

106

PUZZLE No. 193
Black

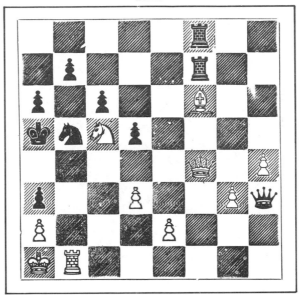

White
White to play and mate in five moves.

PUZZLE No. 194
Black

White
White to play and mate in six moves.

107

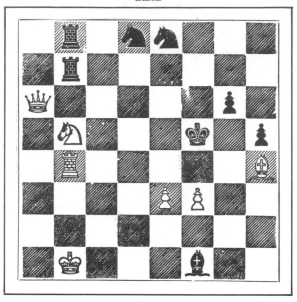

White
White to play and mate in six moves.

PUZZLE No. 196
Black

White
White to play and mate in six moves.

White
White to play and mate in five moves.

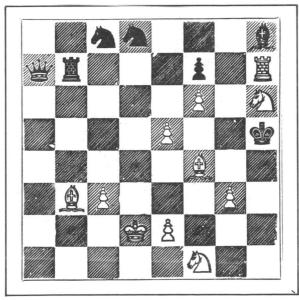

White
White to play and mate in three moves.

PUZZLE No. 199
Black

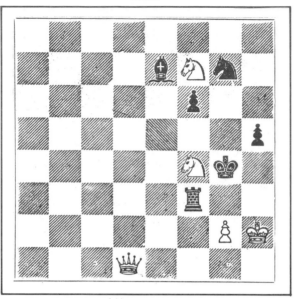

White
White to play and mate in three moves.

PUZZLE No. 200
Black

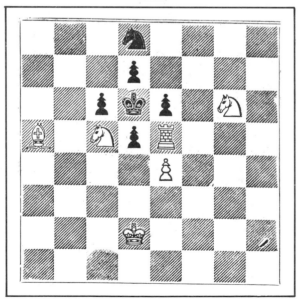

White
White to play and mate in three moves.

110

SOLUTIONS

PUZZLE No. 1

WHITE	BLACK
1. Ktx QBP	KBP moves
2. B—Q3	P x B
3. R—KB4 (ch)	P x R
4. KP mates	

●

PUZZLE No. 2

WHITE	BLACK
1. R—KB5	Q or R x Q(best)
2. R—KB6 (ch)	K—Q4
3. B—QB4 (ch)	K x B*
4. Kt—QKt6. Mate	
*3.	K—K5
4. Kt—Q6. Mate	

Note: This puzzle is clever and leads
to many ingenious combinations.
There is a very commonplace solution,
however, which follows:

1. R—Q6 (ch)	K—B2 (best)
2. Q x QKtP (ch)	R—K2
3. Q x R and mates next move.	

●

PUZZLE No. 3

WHITE	BLACK
1. Kt—Q6	R—KR1 (best)
2. R x Q	P—QB5 (best)
3. R—QKt1— and play as Black can, White will check it with Kt at QKt8 or K5, mating with R next move.	

●

PUZZLE No. 4

WHITE	BLACK
1. Q—K3	P—QB4 (best)
2. B x B	R—K3 (best)
3. Q—Q2 (ch)	K—K5
4. Q—KB4 (ch)	K—Q4
5. P—K4 (ch)	R x KP
6. Q—Q6. Mate	

●

PUZZLE No. 5

WHITE	
1. B x P (ch)	P x B (best)
2. Q—QR1	Q—KKt8 (ch) (best)
3. R covers (dis ch)	Q x Q (best)
4. R—KB5 (ch)	R x R
5. Kt checkmates	

●

PUZZLE No. 6

WHITE	BLACK
1. Kt—KR6 (ch)	P x Kt
2. Q—KR7 (ch)	K—K3
3. B—Q5 (ch)	K x B (best)
4. Q—KB5 (ch)	Q—K4
5. P—K4 (ch) Mate	

●

PUZZLE No. 7

WHITE	BLACK
1. Kt—QB5	K x B
2. Kt—Q7	K—R3
3. Kt—K5	P—KKt3
4. Kt mates	

●

PUZZLE No. 8

White	Black
1. Q—QB3 (ch)	R—QKt6
2. Q—B5 (ch)	R—Kt5
3. Q—K3 (ch)	R—QKt6
4. Q x P (ch)	K—QKt5
5. Q—Q6	K—QKt6
6. Q—Q3. Mate	

●

PUZZLE No. 9

White	Black
1. R from Kt5—Q5	R x R (best)
2. Kt—KKt5 (ch)	K x R
3. Kt—K3 (ch)	K x QP
4. Kt—K6 (ch)	K—QB6
5. B—QR5. Mate	

●

PUZZLE No. 10

White	Black
1. B—QB4	Kt—KKt4
2. QP moves	KBP moves
3. K x Kt	B—Q4
4. R x B. Mate	

●

PUZZLE No. 11

White	Black
1. Q x B (ch)	K x Q (best)
2. QKt—B6	Q x KKt
3. QR x Q	QR—QKt2
4. R—KB8 (ch)	R—QKt1
5. R x R. Mate	

●

PUZZLE No. 12

White	Black
1. Kt—Q1 (ch)	K—Q5
2. Kt—Q5 (dis ch)	K—K4 (best)
3. P—Q4 (ch)	B x P
4. Q—K4 (ch)	P x Q
5. R—KKT5. Mate	

PUZZLE No. 13

White	Black
1. K—QB4	K—B7*
2. Q—KB5 (ch)	K moves
3. Q—KB1 (ch)	K moves
4. Q—Q3. Mate	
*1.	K—R7 or R8
2. Q—QR6 (ch)	K—Kt1
3. K—Q4	K—B7
4. Q—Q3. Mate	

●

PUZZLE No. 14

White	Black
1. B—KB4 (ch)	K—Q4 (best)
2. R—K3	Kt—KB2 (best)
3. K x Kt	P—QR7*
4. B—QB7	Kt—Q1 (ch)
5. K—B6	Kt—B3 (best)
6. P queens (ch)	Kt x Q
7. R—K5. Mate	
*3.	Kt—Q1 (ch)
4. K—B6	Kt—B3 or K3
5. P queens (ch)	Kt x Q
6. R—K5 (ch)	K moves
7. R—KB5. Mate	

●

PUZZLE No. 15

White	Black
1. B—QB7	K—R7 (best)
2. R x QP (dis ch)	K moves
3. R mates	

●

PUZZLE No. 16

WHITE	BLACK
1. Q x R (ch)	Q x Q
2. B x Q	P—K3*
3. P—Q4	P—KB5
4. P—Q5	P x P
5. B—QB3	P—Q5
6. B—Q2. Mate	

*2.	P—KB5
3. P—Q4	P—K3
4. P—Q5	P x P
5. B—QB3, etc.	

PUZZLE No. 17

WHITE	BLACK
1. Q—KB6	Q—KR7*
2. Q x R at B5	Q or B checks
3. P—Kt5 (ch)	Q or B x P (ch)
4. Q x Q or B. Mate	

*Black cannot take the Q, either on its first or second move, without being immediately mated by the Kt. If Black plays 1. Q—K7, or 1. Q—KR7, White checks with its Q at QB3, and mates in two more moves.

PUZZLE NO. 18

WHITE	BLACK
1. R—K4 (ch)	K—B6
2. Kt—KKt5 (ch)	K x Kt
3. Kt—KR3 (ch)	K—B6
4. B—QB6	B—QR4 or
	B—B5 (ch) *
5. R—QKt4 or	
R x B (dis ch)	

* If Back plays Kt—QB5 (ch) White replies with R x Kt (mate). If Black plays Kt—K6, then R—KB4 (mate). Finally, if Black plays Kt or R—KB5, then R x Kt or R (mate)

PUZZLE No. 19

WHITE	BLACK
1. Q—KB3 (ch)	K—K4
2. QKt—QB4 (ch)	K—Q5
3. KKt—K6 (ch)	K x QKt
4. Q—QKt3. Mate	

PUZZLE No. 20

WHITE	BLACK
1. R—QR1	P—QKt3*
2. R x RP (ch)	P x R
3. P—QKt6	R—KKt4 (best)
4. R—KB7	B—QKt1
5. R—QR7 (ch)	B x R
6. P mates	

*1.	K—R2
2. P—QB5	P—QKt3 (best)
3. R—KB7 (ch)	K—R1
4. P x KtP, mating next move	

PUZZLE No. 21

WHITE	BLACK
1. Kt from KB5—Q4	P—QB4
2. Kt—QB6 (ch)	K—K3
3. Kt x QBP. Mate	

PUZZLE No. 22

WHITE	BLACK
1. Q—QB4 (ch)	K x Q
2. Kt—QKt2 (ch)	K—Q5
3. K—B5	Any move
4. B—K3. Mate	

PUZZLE No. 23

WHITE	BLACK
1. K—QB1	K—Kt6
2. Kt—B2	P—R6
3. R x P. Mate	

Note: In this puzzle, by placing the White K on its own square, the position is very much improved, and mate can still be effected in three moves.

•

PUZZLE No. 24

WHITE	BLACK
1. B—KR4	K—Q3
2. B—KKt5	K—K3
3. K—QB5	K—K4
4. R mates	

•

PUZZLE No. 25

WHITE	BLACK
1. R—KB2 (ch)	P x R (best)
2. P—KKt4 (ch)	K x KP
3. P—QB4 (dis ch)	R x B
4. R—K6 (ch)	R x R
5. Kt—Q7. Mate	

•

PUZZLE No. 26

WHITE	BLACK
1. P—Q7	Kt from KB1 x P (best)
2. Kt—QR6	Kt—QR1 (best)
3. P—KKt 4	QKt moves
4. Kt mates at QB5 or QB7 according to which Kt Black has played.	

•

PUZZLE No. 27

WHITE	BLACK
1. R—Q8	R from R4—R3*
2. R x QBP	R from R1—R2
3. B—QKt3	Any move
4. R—B6. Mate	

*1.	B—Q2
2. R—B6 (ch)	B x R
3. Kt—B7. Mate	

Note: Black has other moves, but in each the mate is still inevitable in the given number of moves.

•

PUZZLE No. 28

WHITE	BLACK
1. Kt—Q6 (ch)	Q x Kt
2. P—KB3 (ch)	P x P
3. R—B4 (ch)	Kt or Q x R
4. B or Kt mates according to Black's last move.	

•

PUZZLE No. 29

WHITE	BLACK
1. K—QR8	P—KR3 (best)
2. K—QKt8	P—KR4*
3. Q mates	

| *2. | R moves |
| 3. Q x KRP. Mate | |

•

PUZZLE No. 30

WHITE	BLACK
1. KB—K4	P—Q4
2. QB—Q4	P x KB
3. B—K3	P x P
4. K—QB2	P—B7
5. B—Q2. Mate	

•

116

PUZZLE No. 31

WHITE	BLACK
1. B—QB5	P—Q7
2. Kt—KB2	K—Kt8
3. Kt—Kt4 (Dis ch)	K—B8
4. Kt—KR2. Mate	

PUZZLE No. 32

WHITE	BLACK
1. Kt—Q5	K—K1
2. R—QB8	K—Q2
3. Kt—QKt6 (ch)	K—K3
4. R—QB6	P—B4
5. P Mates	

PUZZLE No. 33

WHITE	BLACK
1. P—KKt6	K xKt
2. R—Q7	B—Kt2
3. R mates	

PUZZLE No. 34

WHITE	BLACK
1. Q—K8 (ch)	R x Q (best)
2. R—KR1	Q x R
3. B—Q1 (ch)	Q x B
4. R—KR4 (ch)	B x R
5. Kt—KB4. Mate	

PUZZLE No. 35

WHITE	BLACK
1. Q—Q5 (ch)	K—B5 (best)
2. P—KB3	P x R (best)
3. K—Kt2	B x Q
4. B—KKt3 (ch)	K—KB4
5. Kt mates	

PUZZLE No. 36

WHITE	BLACK
1. B—KB1	K—K8
2. B—KR3	K—Q8
3. B—Q7	K—K8
4. Kt—KB3 (ch)	K—B8 or K—Q8
5. B mates	

PUZZLE No. 37

WHITE	BLACK
1. K—Kt6	K—R6
2. K—Kt5	K—R7
3. Kt—KB1 (ch)	K—R6
4. Kt—B4. Mate	

PUZZLE No. 38

WHITE	BLACK
1. B—QKt5	RP x B*
2. B—KKt5 (ch)	K x B
3. K x KP	P—Kt5
4. Kt mates	

*1.	K—K2
2. B x QBP	K—Q1 **
3. Kt—Q5	K—QB1
4. R—KR8. Mate	

**2.	K—Kb1
3. R—R8 (ch)	K—K2
4. Mates	

PUZZLE No. 39

WHITE	BLACK
1. B x P (dis ch)	K—KKt3 (best)
2. KBP x P	Any move
3. B moves (dis ch)	K—B4 or K—R4
4. Kt mates	

117

PUZZLE No. 40

White	Black
1. P—Q5	K x KBP
2. Kt—Q4 (ch)	K—K5
3. Kt—KB5	K xKt
4. KB—QB2. Mate	

.

PUZZLE No. 41

White	Black
1. R—Q5	K—QB3
2. K—QB8	P—Q3
3. B—Q7. Mate	

.

PUZZLE No. 42

White	Black
1. K—Kt2	K moves
2. R—QR1 (ch)	K moves
3. R—QR4	K x R
4. B—Q7 (ch)	P—QKt4
5. B—K4	P—KR8
6. B mates	

.

PUZZLE No. 43

White	Black
1. Q—K8 (ch)	R x Q (best)
2. Kt—QB5 (ch)	K—B3 *
3. P—KKt5 (ch)	K x P
4. Kt—K4 (ch)	K—R5 (best)
5. B—QKt4 (ch)	R—KKt1
6. B—K1 (ch)	R interposes
7. B x R. Mate	

*2. | K—Q4
3. B—K4 (ch) | K—Q5
4. Kt—K2. Mate

.

PUZZLE No. 44

White	Black
1. P—K8 and	P—QB8 and
queens	queens
2. Q—KR5 (ch)	K—QB7 (best)
3. Q—KB5 (ch)	K—Q8 (best)
4. Q—KB3 (ch)	K—QB7
5. Q—QKt3 (ch),	
winning the Q, etc.	

.

PUZZLE No. 45

White	Black
1. Q—KB8 (ch)	Q x Q
2. R x Q (ch)	K—Kt2
3. B—KR6 (ch)	K x B
4. R—KKt8 (a	Any move
beautiful coup de	
repos)	
5. R—KR5 (ch)	B x R
6. P—KKt5. Mate	

.

PUZZLE No. 46

· White	Black
1. R—Q5	P—QB5 (best)
2. Q—QKt7	P x R (best)
3. Q—KR7	Q x Kt *
4. Q—KR1 (ch)	R x Q
5. B mates	

*3. | P—Q5
4. Kt—K7 (ch). Mate

.

PUZZLE No. 47

White	Black
1. P—KKt6 (ch)	K x P
2. Q—KB5 (ch)	K x Q
3. KB—K4 (ch)	K—K4
4. Kt—Q3 (ch)	K x B
5. KRP x P	Any move
6. P—KB5. Mate	

PUZZLE No. 48

WHITE	BLACK
1. R—K3	Kt interposes (best)
2. P—KKt7	R—KKt1 *
3. R x Kt (ch)	QP x R
4. R x KP (ch)	Q x R
5. Kt x QBP. Mate	

*2.	QP x QBP
3. QKt P x P	R—KKt1 (best)
4. R x Kt (ch)	Q x R
5. R x Q, or Kt x P	

•

PUZZLE No. 49

WHITE	BLACK
1. R—QB6 (ch)	K x R
2. Kt—K5 (ch)	K—QKt3
3. B—Q4 (ch)	P—QB4
4. Kt—QB4 (ch)	Q x Kt *
5. R—Q6, takes P and mates	

*4.	K x P
5. Kt mates	

•

PUZZLE No. 50

WHITE	BLACK
1. Kt—KR6 (ch)	R x Kt
2. B—Q7 (ch)	R—KB4 (dis ch)
3. K—QKt5 (dis ch)	P—QB5 (dis ch)
4. R—QB5	Q—K3 *
5. Q—Q1 (ch)	Q or R interposes
6. Q x Q or Q x R. Mate	

*4.	Black has many other modes of play here, but none which can prevent the mate in six moves.

•

PUZZLE No. 51

WHITE	BLACK
1. Kt—KB8	P—KR6
2. K—K4	K—Kt5
3. QB—K3	K—R4
4. K—B4	K—R3
5. K—Kt4 (dis ch) Mate	

•

PUZZLE No. 52

WHITE	BLACK
1. Q—KKt6	B x KB *
2. Q x KRP (ch)	B—KR2
3. Q—KB8 (ch)	B—KKt1
4. Kt—KB7 (ch)	K—KR2
5. Kt—KKt5 (ch)	K—KR1
6. Q—KR6 (ch)	B—KR2
7. Q x B. Mate	

*Any other play would allow White to mate on the next move.

•

PUZZLE No. 53

WHITE	BLACK
1. Kt—K7 (ch)	K—K5
2. Kt—KB5	P x P
3. K—KR4	R—K3
4. Q—KKt2 (ch)	K x Kt
5. Q—KKt4. Mate	

•

PUZZLE No. 54

WHITE	BLACK
1. Kt—KR5 (ch)	P x Kt (best)
2. R—Q5 (dis ch)	K—K3
3. P x P (ch)	K x R
4. R—KKt1	Any move
5. R—Q1. Mate	

•

PUZZLE No. 55

WHITE	BLACK
1. B—KR2	B—K2 (best)
2. R—KB3	R—KKt4 (best)
3. R x KBP	R—QB1 (best)
4. R—QR6	Kt—QKt6 (best)
5. R x P (ch)	Kt x R
6. P mates	

PUZZLE No. 56

WHITE	BLACK
1. K x P (dis ch)	K x Kt
2. K x R (dis ch)	K—Q5 (best)
3. K x Kt (dis ch)	K—QB6
4. K x R (dis ch)	
Mate	

PUZZLE No. 57

WHITE	BLACK
1. R x Kt (ch)	K—QB4 (best)
2. R—QB3 (ch)	P x R
3. P—Q4 (ch)	P x P (e.p.)
4. Kt—Q7 (ch)	R x Kt (best)
5. Kt—QB7	Any move
6. Q or Kt mates	

PUZZLE No. 58

WHITE	BLACK
1. B—QR6	KR—KR5 (best)
2. R—QKt5 (ch)	K—B5
3. R—QKt8 (dis ch)	K—B4
4. Kt x P (ch)	K—B3
5. B—QKt5. Mate	

PUZZLE No. 59

WHITE	BLACK
1. B—Q5 (ch)	Kt—K3
2. R x Kt	K moves
3. B—QB4	K—B2
4. R—K4 (dis ch)	K—B1
5. B—KKt8	K x B
6. R—KB4	K—R1
7. R mates	

PUZZLE No. 60

WHITE	BLACK
1. P—QB4 (ch)	P x P
2. R—K3	Q—KKt7 *
3. Q x Q	B x Q (best)
4. Kt from KR4—KB5	B x KRP
5. R x QB	Any move
6. Kt—K7. Mate	

*2.	B x Q
3. KKt—KB5	Q x R
4. P x Q	Any move
5. Kt—K7. Mate	

PUZZLE No. 61

WHITE	BLACK
1. Q—Q6 (ch)	P x Q
2. R—KB5 (ch)	K x R
3. Kt x P (ch)	K moves
4. Kt—QB4 (dbl ch)	K moves
5. Kt—KKt3. Mate	

PUZZLE No. 62

WHITE	BLACK
1. B—QB6 (ch)	P x B
2. R—QB5 (ch)	B x R
3. Kt—K4	Any move
4. One of the Kts mates	

PUZZLE No. 63

WHITE	BLACK
1. Kt—QB6 (ch)	K—QB6 (best)
2. Kt—Q5 (ch)	K—QB5
3. Kt—K3 (ch)	K—B6
4. R x B	Any move
5. Kt—Q1. Mate	

PUZZLE No. 64

WHITE	BLACK
1. Q—KB2 (ch)	K—Kt5
2. K x QP	K—KR4
3. Q—Q4	K—KR3
4. Q—KR8. Mate	

PUZZLE No. 65

WHITE	BLACK
1. Q—KKt6	Q x Q(best)
2. K x Q (dis ch)	K—Kt1
3. Kt—R6 (ch)	K—R1
4. Kt—B7 (ch)	K—Kt1
5. R—KR8 (ch)	B x R
6. Kt mates	

PUZZLE No. 66

WHITE	BLACK
1. Q—K1 (ch)	K—QR3 (best)
2. Kt—QKt8 (ch)	K—Kt3
3. P—QR5 (ch)	K—QB2
4. Q—KKt3. Mate	

PUZZLE No. 67

WHITE	BLACK
1. K—KB6	K—Q4
2. Kt—KB7	K moves
3. Kt—Kt8 (ch)	K moves
4. K—K7	K moves
5. R mates	

PUZZLE No. 68

WHITE	BLACK
1. Q—KR4	K—QR3
2. Q—KR7	K—QR4
3. Q—K4	K—QR3
4. Q—QR8. Mate	

PUZZLE No. 69

WHITE	BLACK
1. B—Q8 (ch)	R—KKt4
2. Kt—Q7	P—KR4
3. Kt—K5	P—KR3
4. Kt—KKt4	P x Kt
5. R—KR3 (ch)	P x R
6. P—KKt3. Mate	

PUZZLE No. 70

WHITE	BLACK
1. Kt—K5	P moves
2. R—KB3	P moves
3. Kt—Q3	P x R
4. Kt mates	

PUZZLE No. 71

WHITE	BLACK
1. Q—QB4	R—QR5 *
2. Q—KB1	KBP x P (best)
3. Q—KB8	Kt—KB2 (best)
4. Q—QKt8 (ch)	R—Q3
5. Kt—Q7. Mate	

*1.	Kt x Kt **
2. Q x Kt (ch)	R—Q4
3. Q—Q6 (ch)	R x Q
4. B x R. Mate	

** If P—KB4, White plays Kt—KKt4 (ch), etc.

•

PUZZLE No. 72

WHITE	BLACK
1. Q—K7 (ch)	R—Q3
2. Q—K5 (ch)	Q—Q4 (best)
3. K—Q3	Any move
4. R mates	

•

PUZZLE No. 73

WHITE	BLACK
1. B—K7	Kt x B (best)
2. Kt—KB6 (ch)	K—Q1
3. Kt—Q4	Kt—KKt4
4. K—QKt7	Either Kt moves
5. Kt mates at the K6 or QB6	

•

PUZZLE NO. 74

WHITE	BLACK
1. B—QB3	K moves
2. B—QB6	K moves
3. B—QKt5	K moves
4. P—K4 (ch)	K moves
5. P—Q4. Mate	

•

PUZZLE No. 75

WHITE	BLACK
1. Kt—KB5 (ch)	K—QB4
2. Kt—Q3 (ch)	K—Q4
3. P x Kt (ch)	K x R
4. B—QB2, and mates by dis. ch. next move, no matter what Black plays.	

•

PUZZLE No. 76

WHITE	BLACK
1. Kt—Kt3 (ch)	K—K8 (best)
2. Q—K8	P—QR4
3. Q—K7	Any move
4. Kt or Q mates	

•

PUZZLE No. 77

WHITE	BLACK
1. B x B (ch)	K x B (best)
2. R—QB7	Any move (for example, K x Kt)
3. R—KKt7	Any move
4. P—Kt4 (ch)	R x P
5. P x R. Mate	

•

PUZZLE No. 78

WHITE	BLACK
1. P—Q4	B—K3 (ch)(best)
2. K—QKt8	B—Q2 (best)
3. B x B	K x B
4. K—Kt7	K—Q3
5. R mates	

•

PUZZLE No. 79

White	Black
1. R—Q1	P—QB6
2. R—Q3	P x R *
3. P—KB4. Mate	

*Black has other modes of play, but none to prevent mate next move. If Black moves B, R mates at Q5; if Kt is moved, White's Kt mates at Q7.

•

PUZZLE No. 80

White	Black
1. Q—K3	P—QB5 * ** ***
2. P x P (ch)	K x P
3. Q mates	

*1.	B—KB7
2. Kt—KB4 (ch)	P x Kt
3. Q mates	

**1.	P—K5
2. Q—KKt5 (ch)	B—K5
3. Kt mates	

***1.	B—KR7
2. P—QB4 (ch)	P x P e.p.
3. Q mates	

•

PUZZLE No. 81

White	Black
1. R—QB4	Q—Q5 *
2. Q—K4 (ch)	Q x Q ** ***
3. R mates	

* If Black mates any other move, White mates next move.

**2.	K xR
3. Q x Q. Mate	

***2.	K x Q
3. R x Q.Mate	

•

PUZZLE No. 82

White	Black
1. B—Q5 (dis ch)	K—K4
2. Kt x B (ch)	K—Q5
3. K—Q2	P x P
4. R—Q1	P checks *
5. K—K3 (dis ch). Mate	

*4.	K x B
5. K—K3 (dis ch). Mate	

•

PUZZLE No. 83

White	Black
1. B—QKt7 (ch)	R x B
2. R—QB8 (ch)	R interposes
3. Kt—QB7. Mate	

•

PUZZLE No. 84

White	Black
1. K—KB7	R—KR5
2. Q—KR8 (ch)	K—KKt4
3. Q mates	

•

PUZZLE No. 85

White	Black
1. R—Q7	R—KKt
2. Q—R5	K to corner
3. R x RP	R—QB1
4. B x P (ch)	K moves
5. Q—R8.Mate	

•

PUZZLE No. 86

WHITE	BLACK
1. QB—QB5 (ch)	K—QR1
2. KB x Kt	Q x Q (ch)
3. K—QB7 (ch)	Q interposes
4. B x Q. Mate	

PUZZLE No. 87

WHITE	BLACK
1. R—KKt8 (ch)	K—Kt2
2. Kt—R5 (ch)	K—Kt3
3. R—Kt6 (ch)	P interposes
4. R x P. Mate	

PUZZLE No. 88

WHITE	BLACK
1. Q—Q8 (ch)	K—QR2
2. QKt—QKt5 (ch)	K—QR3
3. Kt x QBP (ch)	K—QR2
4. KKt—QB8 (ch)	B x Kt
5. Kt—QKt5 (ch)	K—QKt2
6. Q—QB7 (ch)	K—QR3
7. Q x B (ch)	K x Kt
8. Q—QB4. Mate	

PUZZLE No. 89

WHITE	BLACK
1. Q—K7 (ch)	K x Q
2. Kt—KKt6 (ch)	K—Q1
3. Kt—KB7 (ch)	K—QB1
4. Kt—K7. Mate	

PUZZLE No. 90

WHITE	BLACK
1. Kt—QB7 (ch)	K—QKt1
2. Q—K8 (ch)	QB—QB1
3. Kt—QR6 (ch)	K—QKt2
4. KB—KKt2 (ch)	K x Kt
5. Q—QKt5 (ch)	Kt x Q
6. QRP x Kt (ch)	K—QR4
7. Kt—QB6. Mate	

PUZZLE No. 91

WHITE	BLACK
1. R—KR8 (ch)	K x R
2. Q—KR6 (ch)	QR—KR2
3. R x KR (ch)	KB x R
4. Q x KB (ch)	Q—KKt3
5. Kt x KKtP. Mate	

PUZZLE No. 92

WHITE	BLACK
1. KR—KR1 (ch)	R interposes *
2. QR—KR7 (ch)	R x QR
3. P mates	

*1.	Kt—KR3
2. QR—QKt8 (ch)	Kt—KKt1
3. KR x Kt. Mate	

PUZZLE No. 93

WHITE	BLACK
1. R—K5	K moves
2. R—K8 (ch)	K moves
3. Kt—Q6 (ch)	K moves
4. P mates	

PUZZLE No. 94

White	Black
1. R—QR8 (ch)	K x R
2. B—Q5 (ch)	K—QKt1
3. B—QR8 (ch)	K x R
4. BP moves one square. Mate	

•

PUZZLE No. 95

White	Black
1. BP becomes a Kt (ch)	R x Kt
2. P x R becomes a Kt (ch)	K to corner *
3. R x Kt (ch)	K—Kt1
4. Kt at B5—R6 (ch)	K x B
5. R—B7 (ch)	K xKt or moves to corner
6. R mates	

*2.	K—Kt1
3. Kt at B5—R6 (ch)	K to corner
4. B x Kt (ch)	K x B
5. R—B7 (ch)	K x Kt
6. R mates	

•

PUZZLE No. 96

White	Black
1. K—KKt6	K moves
2. B—KB6	K moves
3. K—KR7	K moves
4. P moves	K moves
5. B—KKt7 (ch)	K moves
6. P mates	

•

PUZZLE No. 97

White	Black
1. Q—QKt8 (ch)	K—QR3 (best)
2. Q—Q6 (ch)	K—R4 (best)
3. Q—QR3 (ch)	K moves
4. Q—QB5 (ch)	K—QKt2 (best)
5. Q—QB7 (ch)	K—R3
6. Q—QB6 (ch)	K—R4
7. B—QB7 (ch)	K—R5
8. Q—R6 (ch)	K moves
9. Q—R3 (ch)	K moves
10. Q—QB5. Mate	

•

PUZZLE No. 98

White	Black
1. Q x Kt (ch)	K—Kt1 *
2. Kt checks	K—QB1
3. Kt—QKt6 (ch)	K—Kt1
4. Q—QB8 (ch)	R x Q
5. Kt mates	

*1.	Q interposes
2. Q x Q (ch)	Kt—Kt1
3. Kt checks	K—B1
4. Kt—KB8 (dis ch)	K moves
5. Q mates	

•

PUZZLE NO. 99

White	Black
1. B—KKt7 (dis ch)	K—Kt1
2. R—KR8 (ch)	K—KB2
3. R—KB8 (ch)	K—K3
4. R x P at KB6 (ch)	K—Q4
5. R—Q6 (ch)	K—K5
6. R—Q4 (ch)	K—KB6
7. R—KB4 (ch)	K—K7
8. R—KB2 (ch)	K—Q6
9. B—B1 (ch)	K—K5
10. R—KB4 (ch)	K—Q4
11. R—Q4 (ch)	K—K3
12. R—Q6 (ch)	K—KB2
13. R—KB6 (ch)	K—Kt1
14. R—KB8 (ch)	K—R2
15. R—KR8. Mate	

Note: The mate may be deferred one move by interposing the Rook at Black's ninth move.

•

PUZZLE No. 100

White	Black
1. Kt—K7 (ch)	K—B1
2. Kt—Kt6 (ch)	K—Kt1
3. R—K8 (ch)	K—R2
4. Kt—B4 (dis ch)	K—R3
5. KtP mates	

•

PUZZLE No. 101

White	Black
1. R—KB5	R—Q2
2. Q—K6 (ch)	R covers
3. Q x R (ch)	K moves
4. R mates	

•

PUZZLE No. 102

White	Black
1. R x RP (ch)	K x R
2. R—B6 (ch)	K—R2
3. Kt x P (ch)	K moves
4. Kt checks	K—Kt1
5. Kt—R6 (dis ch)	K—R1
6. Q—QKt8 (ch)	R x Q
7. Kt checks	K—R2
8. B mates	

•

PUZZLE No. 103

White	Black
1. R—KKt5 (ch)	K x R
2. Kt—KB7 (ch)	K—R4
3. KKtP mates	

•

PUZZLE No. 104

White	Black
1. QP moves (ch)	B x P
2. R—QKt8 (ch)	K x R
3. QRP moves (ch)	K—QR1
4. Kt mates	

•

PUZZLE No. 105

White	Black
1. Kt—Q8	K moves
2. K—KB3	K moves
3. Kt—KB7 (ch)	K moves
4. P—KKt4. Mate	

•

PUZZLE NO. 106

White	Black
1. Q—Kt7 (ch)	K x Kt
2. B x Kt (ch)	K moves
3. R—Q2 (ch)	K moves
4. B—K4 (ch)	K moves
5. RP mates	

•

PUZZLE No. 107

White	Black
1. Q—KB2	P moves
2. Q—KB7	P moves
3. Q—QR2	P moves
4. R—QKt3	P x R
5. Q—QKt2 (ch)	P x Q. Mate

•

PUZZLE No. 108

WHITE	BLACK
1. Kt—KB4	K moves
2. Kt—K6	K moves
3. Kt—Q4	K moves
4. Kt—QB6	K moves
5. Kt—QKt4	K moves
6. Kt—QR6	K moves
7. R at KR4—KR5	K moves
8. P mates	

•

PUZZLE No. 109

WHITE	BLACK
1. P checks	K x P
2. Kt—KKt8 (dis ch)	K—KR1 *
3. Q—KR6	K x Kt
4. Q—KR7	K x Kt
5. Q—KKt7	K moves
6. R—Q8	K x R
7. Q—K7	K moves
8. Q—Q7	K x B
9. R—QR8	K x R
10. Q—QB8	B interposes
11. B—K4	B x B
12. Q—QKt7	B x Q
13. P x B. Mate	

*2.	K x Kt at KB1
3. Q—K7 (ch)	K x Kt
4. Q—KR7	K moves, etc. as before
5. Q—KKt7	

•

PUZZLE No. 110

WHITE	BLACK
1. Kt—QB6 (ch)	K—K1
2. Q—KB8 (ch)	Q x Q *
3. Kt x B. Mate	

*2.	K x Kt
3. kt—QKt8. Mate	

•

PUZZLE No. 111

WHITE	BLACK
1. B—Q6	K—K6
2. B—K5	K—KB6
3. R—QB2	K—K6
4. R—QB3. Mate	

•

PUZZLE No. 112

WHITE	BLACK
1. R—Q1 (ch)	K—QB5
2. Q—Q3 (ch)	K—QB4
3. Q—Q6 (ch)	K—QB5
4. Q—Q4 (ch)	K moves
5. R—QKt1 (ch)	K moves
6. Q—QKt2 (ch)	P x Q. Mate

•

PUZZLE No. 113

WHITE	BLACK
1. R x R (ch)	Kt x R (best)
2. Q—Q7 (ch)	K x Q
3. R x P (ch)	K—Q1
4. Kt x P. Mate	

•

PUZZLE No. 114

WHITE	BLACK
1. Kт—KKt4 (ch)	R x Kt
2. KR—KB3 (ch)	K x R
3. QR—Q3. Mate	

•

PUZZLE No. 115

WHITE	BLACK
1. Q—K1 (ch)	K—R2
2. QR—QKt2 (ch)	Q covers
3. KR—KKt2 (ch)	Q x KR
4. Q—KKt3 (ch)	K—R1 *
5. KBP x Q (ch)	K—Kt1
6. KRP. Mates	

*If K—Kt1, White moves KRP and mates with KBP.

PUZZLE No. 116

WHITE	BLACK
1. R—KR1 (ch)	Kt covers
2. B—B1 (ch)	Kt covers
3. KBP moves one square	K—KR4
4. R x Kt. Mate	

PUZZLE No. 117

WHITE	BLACK
1. R—Kt6	K—R2
2. P moves	K—R1
3. R—K6	K—Kt1 (best)
4. R—KB6	K—R1 (best)
5. R—B8 (ch)	K—R2
6. R—K8	K x P
7. R—K7	K moves
8. R mates	

PUZZLE No. 118

WHITE	BLACK
1. QKtP moves (ch)	K—QKt3 *
2. KKt—QB4 (ch)	K—QB2
3. QKt—Q5 (ch)	K—Q1
4. KP moves (ch)	K—K1
5. KKt—Q6 (ch)	Kt x Kt
6. B—KKt6 (ch)	Kt covers
7. Kt—QB7. Mate	

* If Black moves to QR4, White mates in two moves.

PUZZLE No. 119

WHITE	BLACK
1. KKt—KB5 (ch)	K—QB4 (best)
2. K—QR3	Any move
3. KKtP moves and mates	

PUZZLE No. 120

WHITE	BLACK
1. R—QB8	K x R
2. R—QB5 (ch)	K—QKt1 (best)
3. R—QB8 (ch)	K x R
4. Q—KR8. Mate	

PUZZLE No. 121

WHITE	BLACK
1. Kt—QB5 (ch)	K—Kt3 (best)
2. Q—QR6 (ch)	K xKt
3. Q—QR5 (ch)	K—Q5
4. B—KB2	K—Q6
5. Q—Q2. Mate	

PUZZLE No. 122

WHITE	BLACK
1. Q—KKt1 (ch)	K x Q
2. R—KR6 (dis ch)	K moves
3. R x RP (ch)	K x R
4. R x Kt (ch)	K moves
5. Kt—KB4. Mate	

PUZZLE No. 123

White	Black
1. Kt—Q7 (ch)	K—QKt2 (best) *
2. Q—KR1 (ch)	R x Q (best)
3. B—QR6 (ch)	K x B
4. Kt—QB5 (ch)	K—QR4
5. P mates	

* If K—QB1 or K—QR1, White mates directly with R.

•

PUZZLE No. 124

White	Black
1. B—K5 (ch)	K—K2 *
2. B—KB6 (ch)	K—K1 (best)
3. Q x KP (ch)	KBP x Q (best)
4. B—KR5 (ch)	B—KKt3
5. B x B. Mate	

* If Kt x B, White mates with Q next move.

•

PUZZLE No. 125

White	Black
1. Q—KB6 (ch)	K x Q *
2. Kt—KKt4 (dbl ch)	K—Kt2
3. R—B7 (ch)	K—Kt1 **
4. Kt—KB6 (ch)	K—R1
5. R x P. Mate	

*1.	K—Q4
2. R—Q1 (ch)	K—QB4
3. Q—Q4 (ch)	K—Kt5
4. R—QKt1 (ch)	K—R6
5. Q—QKt2. Mate	

**3.	K—R1
4. P moves and checks	K—Kt1
5. Kt—R6. Mate	

•

PUZZLE No. 126

White	Black
1. Q x KP (ch)	K x Q
2. Kt—Q6 (ch)	K xKt
3. QBP moves (ch)	K x Kt
4. KP moves becoming a Kt. Mate	

•

PUZZLE No. 127

White	Black
1. R—Q1 (ch)	K—K5 *
2. R—Q4 (ch)	K x R
3. B—QB6	Any move
4. QBP mates	

*1.	R interposes
2. R x R (ch), etc.	K x R

•

PUZZLE No. 128

White	Black
1. R x Kt (ch)	R x R
2. Q—QKt4 (ch)	Kt x Q
3. P xKt (ch)	K—R3
4. P moves (ch)	K—R4
5. K—R3 and mates with P next move	

•

PUZZLE No. 129

White	Black
1. R at KKt1 x B	Q—KKt2 *
2. R—KKt5	Q—KKt3 **
3. R at Kt5 x Q	P x R
4. R x KRP. Mate	

* The only move to prevent checkmate next move.

**2.	Q x Kt (ch)
3. R x Q	RP moves
4. R—KR8. Mate	

PUZZLE No. 130

WHITE	BLACK
1. B—KB8	K—Q5
2. B—KKt7 (ch)	K—K6
3. R—KB6	K—Q5
4. R—KB3 (dis ch). Mate	

•

PUZZLE No. 131

WHITE	BLACK
1. K—QKt7	KP moves
2. Kt x KP	K x P
3. K—Kt6	K—R5
4. Kt—Q7	K—Kt5 (best)
5. Kt—QKt8	K—R5
6. Kt—QR6	P moves
7. Kt mates	

•

PUZZLE No. 132

WHITE	BLACK
1. Q—KKt1 (ch)	B—K6 *
2. Q—KKt7 (ch)	KP moves
3. Q—QR7 (ch)	Kt—QB4
4. Q—QR1 (ch)	P—QB6
5. Q x P. Mate	

*1.	K—K4
2. Q—KKt7 (ch)	K—B5 (best)
3. Q—KKt5 (ch)	K x P
4. Kt x B. Mate	

•

PUZZLE No. 133

WHITE	BLACK
1. K—B3	K—Kt4
2. P—QB4	K—R5 *
3. P—K3	K—Kt4
4. K—Kt3	K—B4
5. K—R4	K—K5
6. B—Kt6. Mate	

*2.	K—B4
3. KP moves one square	K—Kt4
4. K—Kt3, etc, etc.	

•

PUZZLE No. 134

WHITE	BLACK
1. QB—QR3	K—KB4
2. Kt—QKt4 (dis ch)	K—K4
3. KB—K4	K x P
4. Kt—QB6 or Kt—Q3 (dis ch). Mate	

•

PUZZLE No. 135

WHITE	BLACK
1. KKt—K6 (ch)	K—B2 (best)
2. P moves (ch)	K—K1
3. KKt—KKt7 (ch)	K—Q2
4. Q—QB6 (ch)	B x Q
5. P x B (ch)	K—B2
6. KKt—K6 (ch)	K—Kt1
7. QKt—QR6 (ch)	K—R1
8. KKt—QB7. Mate	

•

PUZZLE No. 136

WHITE	BLACK
1. Q—KKt1 (ch)	R x Q (best)
2. B—Q8 (ch)	K—R2
3. B—QKt6 (ch)	K x B
4. QBP moves (ch)	K—R2
5. QR—QR8 (ch)	K x R
6. R—K8 (ch)	K—R2
7. Kt—QB8 (ch)	K—Kt or K—R1
8. Kt—QKt6 (dis ch)	K—R2 or K—B2
9. R mates	

•

PUZZLE No. 137

WHITE	BLACK
1. QB—KB6	KRP moves
2. QB—QKt2	KBP moves
3. K—QB3	K—K4
4. K—QB4 (dis ch).	
Mate	

•

PUZZLE No. 138

WHITE	BLACK
1. Kt—QR6 (ch)	K—R1
2. Kt—QB6	B—QKt3 (best)
3. Q x B	P x Q
4. Kt x QBP. Mate	

•

PUZZLE No. 139

WHITE	BLACK
1. Q x P (ch)	K x Q
2. R—B1 (ch)	K—Kt5
3. R—B4 (ch)	K x R
4. Castles (ch)	K—Kt5
5. Kt—K3 (ch)	K—R5
6. Kt—KB3. Mate	

•

PUZZLE NO. 140

WHITE	BLACK
1. R—QR8	K—QB4
2. B—KB2 (ch)	K—QKt5
3. B—QR7	K—QR4
4. B—QB5 (dis ch).	
Mate	

Note: This is the solutiona called for,
but there is an easier way to give mate
— by first playing the K to B7, then
taking the P with the B, and on the
third move checkmating with the R at
QR5.

•

PUZZLE No. 141

WHITE	BLACK
1. P x P (ch)	K x P
2. Q—KR5 (ch)	K—R2 *
3. Q—KB5. Mate	
*2.	K x Q
3. Kt—KB4. Mate	

•

PUZZLE No. 142

WHITE	BLACK
1. Q—KKt8	Q—K3 (ch)
	(best) *
2. Q x Q (ch)	K x Q
3. Kt—KB5	Kt—Q3
4. Kt x KtP. Mate	
*1.	KP moves
2. Q x Kt and mates	
next move	

•

PUZZLE No. 143

WHITE	BLACK
1. QRP moves (ch)	K—QB5
2. B—KR3	K x Kt
3. B—KB1	K—QB5
4. KP moves (dis ch).	
Mate	

•

PUZZLE No. 144

WHITE	BLACK
1. R—QKt5	K—Q3 *
2. Kt—KB5 (ch)	K—B3
3. R—QKt6 (ch)	K—B4
4. Q—QKt7and mates	
next move	
*1.	R—Q2 **
2. R—QKt6 (ch)	K—B4
3. Q x R and mates	
next move	

131

** If K x R, White mates in two moves. If R—K2, then White plays R—Q5, mating next move.

•

PUZZLE No. 145

WHITE	BLACK
1. Q x P (ch)	K x Q
2. QKt—Q5 (dis ch)	K—Kt1 (best)
3. QKt—KB6 (ch)	K—R1
4. Qkt—KKt4(dis ch)	Kt—K4
5. B x Kt (ch)	K—Kt1 *
6. QKt x RP (ch)	K—R2
7. KKt—KKt5. Mate	

*5.	K—R2
6. KKt—KKt5 (ch)	K—Kt1
7. QKt x RP. Mate	

•

PUZZLE No. 146

WHITE	BLACK
1. B—QR4	K—B4 or K—K5
2. B—QB2 (ch)	K—K4
3. K—Q3	K—B4
4. K—Q4 (dis ch). Mate	

•

PUZZLE No. 147

WHITE	BLACK
1. B—QKt3	One P moves
2. R—KB8	The other P moves
3. B—KB7	K—KB6
4. B—Q5 (dbl ch).Mate	

•

PUZZLE No. 148

WHITE	BLACK
1. B—QKt6	RP moves, becoming a Q *
2. Q—QR6 (ch)	K x Q
3. K—QB6	Any move
4. QKtP mates	

*1.	K x B
2. K—QB8 and mates next move	

•

PUZZLE No. 149

WHITE	BLACK
1. Q—KKt6 (ch)	K—KKt1 (best)
2. Kt—K7 (ch)	K—KR1
3. Q—KB7	R x Q
4. R—Q8 (ch)	Kt—K1 *
5. R x Kt (ch)	R—B1
6. R x R. Mate	

*4.	R—B1
5. R x R (ch)	Kt—Kt1
6. R x Kt. Mate	

•

PUZZLE No. 150

WHITE	BLACK
1. R—QB1	P—KKt8 or any other move
2. Kt—Q6 and then mates either with Kt at Kt7 or QBP, according as Black plays.	

•

PUZZLE No. 151

WHITE	BLACK
1. QR—K1	K x KR (best)
2. KP moves	P x P (e.p.)
3. R—Q1. Mate	

PUZZLE No. 152

White	Black
1. Q—QR4 (ch)	K—Q4
2. Q—K4 (ch)	K—K3
3. QBP moves	Q x R (ch) (best)
4. Q—KKt6 (ch)	K—Q2 (best)
5. Q x Q (ch)	K—QB1
6. Q x QKtP. Mate	

·

PUZZLE No. 153

White	Black
1. Kt—Q3 (ch)	K—Q5
2. P x P (ch)	P x P
3. B—QR3	R from R2 to R3*
4. Q—QB5 (ch)	R x Q
5. B x R. Mate	

*3.	Kt x Q
4. Kt—K6. Mate	

·

PUZZLE NO. 154

White	Black
1. Q—KB6	R x P (best)
2. Q x B (ch)	R—Kt5 *
3. Q—KB2	Any move
4. Q or Kt mates	

*2.	Kt—Kt5
3. Q x R	Any move
4. Kt or Q mates	

·

PUZZLE No. 155

White	Black
1. Kt—QB7 (ch)	K—QB5
2. QP moves (ch)	K—Q5
3. Q—KB5	Q—K4 (best)
4. KKt—K6 (ch)	Q x Kt *
5. Kt mates	

* If Black plays R x Kt, the result will be the same.

PUZZLE No. 156

White	Black
1. Kt—KR4	K—Q4
2. Q—Q6 (ch)	K—K5
3. Q—Q4. Mate	

·

PUZZLE No. 157

White	Black
1. Q—KKt5 (ch)	K x Kt (best)
2. Q x B (ch)	K x Q
3. B x QKtP (ch). Mate	

·

PUZZLE No. 158

White	Black
1. Kt—B6 (ch)	Kt x Kt
2. Kt x Kt (ch)	K—R1
3. Q—KR4	R—KKt1
4. B—KB8	R—KKt2 (best)
5. Q—KR6	QR x B
6. Kt x KRP	KBP two
7. Kt—KB6 (dis ch)	R—KR2
8. Q x R. Mate	

·

PUZZLE NO. 159

White	Black
1. Kt from Kt3—B5 (ch)	K—Kt5
2. Kt—Q3 (ch)	K—B5 (best)
3. Kt—Q6 (ch)	K—Q4
4. Kt—KB4 (ch)	K x P
5. Kt—KB7 (ch)	K—B4
6. P x P	Any move
7. KKtP mates	

PUZZLE No. 160

WHITE	BLACK
1. QP x P (dis ch)	K—Kt3 (best)
2. Q—QKt4 (ch)	K—R2
3. Kt—QB6 (ch)	Q x Kt
4. Q—QKt8 (ch)	R x Q
5. P—B8, becoming a Kt and giving double check and mate	

•

PUZZLE No. 161

WHITE	BLACK
1. Kt—QB8 (ch)	K—B3
2. Q x R (ch)	K—Kt2 (best)
3. Q—QB3 (ch)	Q interposes
4. Q x Q (ch)	K x Q
5. B—Kt2 (ch). Mate	

•

PUZZLE No. 162

WHITE	BLACK
1. R—K5 (ch)	K x R
2. B—KKt4	QP x P (best)
3. B—Q6 (ch)	K—Q5
4. B—K2 and mates next move	Any move

•

PUZZLE No. 163

WHITE	BLACK
1. B—KB6 (ch)	K—Kt5
2. P x KBP (ch)	K—B5
3. QBP moves	QBP moves(best)
4. QBP moves	Any move
5. Kt mates	

•

PUZZLE No. 164

WHITE	BLACK
1. R—QR4	K x R *
2. R—Q5 (dis ch)	
*1.	Q—K5 **
2. R—Q3 (dis ch)	
**1.	Q—KKt1
2. Kt—Q3. Mate	

•

PUZZLE No. 165

WHITE	BLACK
1. Castles	Castles
2. R—KKt1 (ch)	K—R1
3. B checks	R interposes
4. B x R (ch). Mate	

•

PUZZLE No. 166

WHITE	BLACK
1. R—Q8. {This is the key move. No matter how White now plays, Black must win.}	R x P *
2. R—Q7 (ch and wins)	

*1.   R—R6 (ch)
2. R—Q3, and if White takes Black's pawn, checks with R at Q7, and wins as before.

•

PUZZLE No. 167

WHITE	BLACK
1. K—QR2	Kt x Q (best)
2. Kt—B6 (ch)	K—QR1
3. B—QB8	R—QR5 (ch)
4. R—QR3	Kt—QB6 (ch) *
5. P x Kt	R x R (ch)
6. K x R	B—QB4 (ch)
7. K—Kt3	Any move
8. B—Kt7. Mate	

* If Black takes R, Black will be
mated in one move less.

•

<u>PUZZLE NO. 168</u>

White	Black
1. Q—QB8 (ch)	B—K3
2. Q x B (ch)	P x Q
3. Kt—KKt4	Any move
4. Kt—K3 or	
Kt—R6. Mate	

•

<u>PUZZLE No. 169</u>

White	Black
1. Q—QR5	Q x Q (best)
2. P—Q7 and play	Any move
as Black will, White	
will mate next move	
either by taking Kt	
with P and calling	
for a Q, or by the P	
on to the 8th square,	
making a Kt	

•

<u>PUZZLE No. 170</u>

White	Black
1. Q x B (ch)	K—K4 *
2. Q—KB6 (ch)	K xKt **
3. B—K3 (ch)	K x B (best)
4. Q x Kt (ch)	K—KB5
5. Q—KKt3. Mate	

* If K—Kt2, or if Kt is interposed,
mate follows in fewer moves.

** If Q is taken, White can mate next
move with B

•

<u>PUZZLE No. 171</u>

White	Black
1. R—QB8	R x Q *
2. R x R (ch)	K—Kt2
3. R—KKt8 (ch)	K x Kt
4. Kt—KB5	K—KR4
5. P—KKt4. Mate	

*1.	R x R **
2. Q x R (ch)	K—Kt2 ***
3. Q—KKt8 (ch)	K xKt
4. Kt—B5 (ch)	K—R4
5. P mates	

** Black has many other moves of
defense, but none which can postpone
the mate beyond five moves.

***2.	R—K1
3. Q x R	K—Kt2
4. KKt mates	

•

<u>PUZZLE No. 172</u>

White	Black
1. R x Kt (ch)	B x R
2. Kt—KB2 (ch)	K x P
3. P x P (ch)	R x P
4. B xKt (dis ch)	K x Kt
5. B—KR7. Mate	

•

<u>PUZZLE No. 173</u>

White	Black
1. K—QB7	K—B4 *
2. Kt—Q3 (ch)	K—Q4
3. B—KKt7	K—K3
4. Kt—KB4 (ch)	K—K2
5. K—B6	K—Q1
6. B—KB6. Mate	

*1.	K—K3
2. Kt—Q3	K—Q4 or K—K2
3. B—KKt7	K—K3
4. Kt—KB4 (ch) etc,	
etc.	

PUZZLE No. 174

White	Black
1. Kt—KR6	K—K4
2. QB—QB1	K—Q4 *
3. QB—QKt2	K—K4
4. K—B4 (dis ch)	

*2.	P—K6
3. K—B4 and mates next move	

PUZZLE No. 175

White	Black
1. B—QKt6	Q—Q5
2. KR—QB5	R—KKt4 *
3. QR x KP (ch)	R—K4
4. KR x R (ch). Mate	

* Black has a great variety of defensive moves: B—QB3 to interpose when R checks, or Kt—QB6 for the same purpose, etc., but the result is still the same, mate is forced in four moves.

PUZZLE No. 176

White	Black
1. Kt—QB5	KRP moves
2. B—QB2	P moves, becoming a Q
3. Kt x Q	P moves
4. B x P at KKt6	P moves
5. Kt—KB2	P becomes a Q
6. Kt—Q3. Mate	

PUZZLE No. 177

White	Black
1. R—KKt8 (ch)	K—QB2
2. Kt—QKt5 (ch)	K—QKt1
3. Kt—Q7 (dbl ch)	K—R1
4. Q—QKt8 (ch)	R x Q
5. Kt—QB7 (ch)	R x Kt
6. Kt—QKt6 (ch)	P x Kt (ch)
7. K x P (dis ch)	Q x R
8. R x R (ch)	R must x R and White is stalemated

PUZZLE No. 178

White	Black
1. Kt—QB7 (dis ch)	K x Kt
2. Kt—Q5 (ch)	K—Q3 (best)
3. Q—K6 (ch)	Q x Q
4. Kt—QB7 (dbl ch)	K—Q6
5. Kt—K8 (ch)	R x Kt (best)
6. P x R, becoming a Kt (ch)	K—QB3
7. B—Q5. Mate	

PUZZLE No. 179

White	Black
1. Kt—KB4 (ch)	K—B3
2. Kt—KR5 (ch)	K—K3
3. R—K2 (ch)	K—Q4
4. Kt—KB4 (ch)	K—QB3
5. P—Q8, becoming a Kt (dbl ch and mate)	

PUZZLE No. 180

White	Black
1. Kt—KB7 (ch)	K—B4
2. Kt—KR6 (ch)	K—K4
3. P—QB4 (ch)	R—K1 or KBP moves *
4. R x KP (dbl ch)	K x R
5. KBP moves and mates	

*If QP moves, then 4. R x QP (dbl ch and mate)

•

PUZZLE No. 181

White	Black
1. Kt—K7 (ch)	K—R1
2. B—KB7	Q—Q8 *
3. Kt—Kt6 (ch)	P x Kt
4. R—R4 (ch)	P x R
5. R—R3 (ch). Mate	

* Black has no better move to prolong the mate

•

PUZZLE No. 182

White	Black
1. Kt—Q3	Black's moves
2. Kt—QB1	are all forced
3. Kt x QKtP	
4. Kt—QR5	
5. K x P	
6. Kt—QB6 (ch)	
7. The other Kt mates at QB7	

•

PUZZLE No. 183

White	Black
1. K—QB7	P moves
2. R—KR3	P moves
3. R—K3 and mates with R or QP next move	

•

PUZZLE No. 184

White	Black
1. P x P (dis ch)	K—B4 (best)
2. P x P (ch)	K—Q3 (best)
3. R—Q5 (ch)	K x R
4. P x Kt (dis ch)	K—B4
5. R—QB4 (ch)	K—Q3
6. P x B, becoming a Kt and giving dbl ch and mate	

•

PUZZLE No. 185

White	Black
1. R—K2 (ch)	R x Q (best)
2. B—Q4 (ch)	R x B
3. R—K6 (ch)	Q x R
4. Kt—KR7. Mate	

•

PUZZLE NO. 186

White	Black
1. R—QKt4	Kt x R (best)
2. P x Kt (ch)	K—B5
3. Q—QR3	P—QB4
4. K—K4	P x P
5. Q—K3	P—QKt6
6. Q—Q4. Mate	

•

PUZZLE No. 187

White	Black
1. Q—QR2 (ch)	R x Q
2. R—K5 (ch)	R x R
3. Kt—KB4 (ch)	K—B4
4. B—KKt6 (ch)	K x Kt
5. KKtP mates	

•

PUZZLE No. 188

WHITE	BLACK
1. Kt x KKtP (dis ch)	K—Kt6 (best)
2. Kt—KB3 (dis ch)	K—KR6
3. R—KKt3 (ch)	K x R
4. B—K5 (ch)	K—Kt5 (best)
5. Kt—KB6 (ch)	K—R6
6. P—R8, becoming a Q (ch)	K—Kt7
7. Kt x Kt (dbl ch and mate)	

PUZZLE No. 189

WHITE	BLACK
1. Q—Q1 (ch)	K—QB5
2. Q—Q5 (ch)	K x Q
3. Kt—K3 (ch)	R x Kt
4. R—Q4. Mate	

PUZZLE No. 190

WHITE	BLACK
1. Q—KB8 (ch)	Kt—Kt8
2. Q—QKt4 (ch)	K—B7 or K—B8
3. Q—KB4 (ch)	K—K8
4. K—Kt1	B moves
5. Q—QB1 (ch)	B interposes
6. Q—QB3. Mate	

PUZZLE No. 191

WHITE	BLACK
1. Kt x Kt	K x R (best)
2. K—B6	P—Q8, queening
3. P—K4 (ch)	K x P
4. B—QB6 (checkmate)	

PUZZLE No. 192

WHITE	BLACK
1. R—Q4 (ch)	K x R
2. P—QB4	Q—QR5 *
3. Kt—QKt5 (ch)	Q or B x Kt
4. Kt mates at KB3 or QB2, according to Black's last move	
*2.	P—QR8, becoming a Kt
3. Kt—KB3 (ch)	B x Kt
4. Kt—QKt5. Mate	

PUZZLE No. 193

WHITE	BLACK
1. B—Q4	R x Q (best)
2. Kt x P (ch)	K—QR5
3. B—QKt6	R—QB5
4. P x R	P x P
5. Kt x P. Mate	

PUZZLE No. 194

WHITE	BLACK
1. Kt—Q4 (ch)	K—K4
2. B—KKt3 (ch)	K—Q4
3. P—K4 (ch)	K—B4
4. Kt—QKt3 (ch)	K x R
5. B—K1 (ch)	K x Kt
6. Q—QR2 (ch). Mate	

PUZZLE No. 195

WHITE	BLACK
1. Kt—Q4 (ch)	K—K4
2. B—KKt3 (ch)	K—Q4
3. P—K4 (ch)	K—B4
4. Kt—QKt3 (ch)	K x R
5. B—K1 (ch)	K x Kt
6. Q—QR2 (ch). Mate	

PUZZLE No. 196

WHITE	BLACK
1. Kt—QR6	K x Kt (best)
2. B—QB8 (ch)	K—R4
3. Kt—QB3	P—QR3
4. Kt—Kt5	P x Kt
5. B—QKt7	KtP moves
6. P xP. Mate	

•

PUZZLE No. 197

WHITE	BLACK
1. Q x R (ch)	Q x Q
2. R x Q (ch)	K x R
3. K—K7	B x R (best)
4. K—B7	B moves
5. P—KKt4. Mate	

•

PUZZLE No. 198

WHITE	BLACK
1. Kt—KB5 (dis ch)	K—Kt3 *
2. B—QB2, and no matter how it plays, Black must be mated by the discovered check of B	

*1.	K—Kt5
2. Kt—K3 (ch)	Q x Kt (ch)
3. Kt x Q. Mate	

•

PUZZLE No. 199

WHITE	BLACK
1. Q—K2	K—B4 or K—R5, or B—Q3 *
2. P x R	Any move
3. Q or Kt mates	

* These are Black's best defenses

•

PUZZLE No. 200

WHITE	BLACK
1. B—QKt6	P—Q5 (best)
(threatening mate if P xP or Kt moves)	
2. B x Kt	P—Q6
3. Kt—QKt7. Mate	

•

INDEX

INDEX

References are to puzzle number and not to page